
BIOCHEMISTRY DIVISION

General Editors: P. CAMPBELL AND K. S. DODGSON

Biochemical Approaches to Cancer

The British Empire Cancer Campaign for Research are receiving the author's royalties from this book

Biochemical Approaches to Cancer

BY

ERIC REID, D.Sc.

Biochemistry Unit, Battersea College of Technology, London S.W.11
formerly of the Chester Beatty Research Institute (Institute of Cancer Research, Royal Cancer Hospital) London S.W.3

PERGAMON PRESS

OXFORD · LONDON · EDINBURGH · NEW YORK
PARIS · FRANKFURT

Pergamon Press Ltd., Headington Hill Hall, Oxford
4 & 5 Fitzroy Square, London W.1

Pergamon Press (Scotland) Ltd., 2 & 3 Teviot Place, Edinburgh 1

Pergamon Press Inc., 44-01 21st Street, Long Island City, New York 11101

Pergamon Press S.A.R.L., 24 rue des Ecoles, Paris 5e

Pergamon Press GmbH, Kaiserstrasse 75, Frankfurt-am-Main

First edition 1965
Library of Congress Catalog Card No. 65-24229

Set in 10 on 12 point Times and
Printed in Great Britain by The Alden Press Ltd., Oxford

(2488/65)

Contents

Preface

THIS book, which was undertaken at the suggestion of Dr. P. N. Campbell, is envisaged as being of help on the one hand to established research workers, and on the other hand to students (undergraduate or postgraduate) having a fair acquaintance with biochemistry and seeking an introduction to the cancer field. The layman inquiring about cancer is already well provided for, by books such as those of R. J. C. Harris (*Cancer: The Nature of the Problem*, Penguin Books, 1964), and I. Hieger (*One in Six*, Allan Wingate Ltd, 1955). For readers with a chemical background, there already exist several books (certain of which will be cited later) centered on carcinogens. Few books, however, deal with cancer from the viewpoint of metabolic derangements—this being the central theme in the present book. No apology is made for the scant consideration now given to the vast literature on comparisons of sundry tumours with uncritically chosen normal tissues, and for the emphasis now placed on comparisons that may elucidate how cells of a given type are transformed into cancer cells.

For further reading, there exist a number of useful books and reviews, a few of which are listed in the References. Publications based on symposia are, in general, less useful for filling in the background; all too often it would appear that the symposium was over-ambitious in scope, with much poorly integrated or even irrelevant material. In connection with the ever-rising flood of original papers, the author feels it deplorable that certain journals publish papers in facsimile, with no opportunity for correction of scientific or typographical mistakes; thus, in one such communication, concerning "... Rat Liver, Novikoff Hepatoma, and Adenocarcinomas", there is mention in the text of kidney but nowhere of liver! The real answer lies in self-discipline — a quality to which the present author lays no claim.

In connexion with the present book, the author would be glad to hear of mistakes — these, together with the opinions expressed, being solely his responsibility, although valuable comments on the manuscript were received from Dr. D. A. G. Galton (Chapters 1, 2 and 9), Dr. B. Green, Professor Frank Dickens, F.R.S., Mr. M. K. Turner, and especially (in connexion with Chapters 1, 2, 3, 8 and 9) Dr. P. N. Magee.

Abbreviations are in general restricted to those in current biochemical use, as allowed by the *Biochemical Journal*, It should be noted that, with revision of nomenclature, DPN, DPNH, TPN and TPNH have become NAD, $NADH_2$, NADP and $NADPH_2$ respectively. Less common abbreviations, such as are occasionally used for carcinogens, are explained within the section where they occur. *Chemical compounds* are usually designated by old-established trivial names, but where systematic names are given an attempt has been made (with help from Dr. Joan Reid over certain difficulties) to follow current practice. "Oxo-" is generally used in place of "keto-". *Enzymes* are likewise designated by trivial names, with inclusion of Enzyme Commission numbers in the Index.

References have been kept to a minimum by the citation, where-ever possible, not of original papers (numbered 51 onwards) but of books or reviews (numbered 1–50), or else of original papers — of which some cite earlier papers from the same laboratory covering the work mentioned, and others, as denoted by *italicized* reference numbers, were published from a different laboratory but cite the work in question. Often, however, the reader may prefer to track down the original reference by using the Author Indices (Cumulative Indices may be helpful) in Chemical Abstracts or other abstracts. Inclusion of an author index in the present book would be pointless in view of the scheme adopted to avoid an enormous reference list — a scheme which may tax the reader's patience but saves considerable cost.

Special acknowledgments. For Plates 2 and 3, acknowledgments are given in the legends. Permission to use Figures was kindly given both by the authors concerned (cf. references cited in the legends) and by the respective publishers, viz. Pergamon Press (Figs. 1, 8, 12 and 13), J. & A. Churchill (Fig. 2), The British Council (Fig. 6), The American Association for the Advancement of Science (Fig. 9), Cancer Research Inc., per the Editor (Figs. 7 and 10), H. K. Lewis (Fig. 11, also Plate 1), and the Royal Institute of Chemistry (Fig. 14). The preparation of the manuscript was greatly helped by various forms of assistance, including loan to the author of certain papers (refs. 38, 40, 104, *inter alia*) prior to publication, careful typewriting (Mrs. M. Crampton, Mrs. A. Inglefield and Miss C. Lane), and proofreading and indexing (by Dr. Barbara Mullock).

CHAPTER 1

The Nature of Cancer

Basic Concepts and Terminology

CANCER or *neoplasia* is essentially a process of unrestrained cell division, usually giving rise to a solid tumour. In most tissues the proliferating neoplastic cells remain in contact with one another, eventually forming a tumour. A proportion of the cells, however, lack adhesiveness and become easily detached from the main mass (see below, *metastases*). The cells of the haemopoietic tissues are freely mobile, and show little or no tendency to adhere to one another. Accordingly, in the leukaemias and malignant lymphomas, which are neoplastic conditions of the haemopoietic tissues, tumours are often absent, but the blood contains leucocytes and lymphocytes respectively in vastly increased number. Other publications (e.g. ref. 49) should be consulted for amplification of the following survey.

A *benign* tumour is localized, slow-growing, well-differentiated and generally harmless throughout the lifespan of the organism. Benign "cancer" is essentially an exaggeration of the process of *hyperplasia*, whereby an organ grows by cell division (rather than by cell enlargement, termed hypertrophy) and which is of normal occurrence even in adult animals as, for example, when the uterine lining grows in response to hormonal influences. *Malignant* tumours, on the other hand, invariably endanger the life of the organism, although at first they may be hard to distinguish from benign tumours. The growth may obliterate the organ in which it arises, may impair the function of adjoining organs by sheer pressure, or — most serious of all — may shed cells which, travelling usually by way of the blood or lymph vessels, take root as *metastases* elsewhere in the organism. Malignant growths and their metastases vary in the extent to which they retain the structure and the functional capacity of the tissue in which they originated; but frequently there is *anaplasia* or loss of the characteristic tissue structure (dedifferentiation).

A malignant tumour is termed a *carcinoma* if it arises in epithelial tissue such as skin or breast, and a *sarcoma* if it arises from non-haemopoietic mesenchymal tissues, e.g. connective, skeletal, vascular, meningeal and muscular tissues. (A benign tumour of the skin is termed a *papilloma*. Nerve tumours and other rare types will not be considered here.)

Wherever possible, tumours are classified according to their known or guessed cellular origin. For example, a malignant tumour arising in striated muscle cells may be termed a *rhabdomyosarcoma* (or, loosely, a rhabdosarcoma). Hepatic (parenchymal) cells in the liver are believed to be the source of a *hepatocarcinoma* (further classified as an adenocarcinoma if the tumour histologically resembles glandular tissue); the term *hepatoma* in its strict sense implies a benign growth. The designation of a tumour as benign or malignant is often a matter of arbitrary judgment, and sometimes — as in the present book — the suffix "-oma" is loosely used in place of "-carcinoma" or "-sarcoma" to denote a tumour which in fact may be malignant. A liver tumour which appears to have arisen from bile-duct dells is termed a *cholangiocarcinoma* or *cholangioma*.

Concepts derived from cancer research (oncology). An important aspect of cancer research is the discovery of *carcinogens* or cancer-producing agents (Chapter 3; the term cancerogens as occasionally used is perhaps preferable), many of which (such as certain azo dyes, usually fed in the diet) are valuable tools in experimental work. The term *autochthonous* ("formed where found") applies both to *primary induced* tumours and to *spontaneous* tumours such as arise in the livers or breasts of genetically prone strains of mice. The mention in one review[30] of "a spontaneous azo-dye tumor" is an unfortunate oversight! So-called spontaneous tumours may, of course, be due to the operation of undetected agents.

Whereas some agents are actual *initiators* of cancer, when, for example, trace amounts in an inert solvent are applied to the skin, there are other agents which are not themselves carcinogenic but which boost or synergize the action of carcinogens (initiators) even if the latter are given in sub-carcinogenic doses. These agents, termed *cocarcinogens* or *promoters*, have been most studied in the context of skin cancer. They include not only chemical materials, of which the classical example is croton oil, but also physical influences such as mechanical injury or even ultraviolet light. Hormones may also play a role, as shown by the observation from I. Berenblum's laboratory[21] that deficiency of corticosteroids promotes skin carcinogenesis (by 7,12-dimethylbenzanthracene) although it has no effect on the "initiation" stage. Promoting activity in chemical carcinogenesis has also been shown for some common viruses (W. R. Bryan[21]).

A long *latent period* commonly elapses before tumours appear in response to exposure to a carcinogen (although not with certain viruses such as the polyoma). The time is only moderately shortened by increasing the intensity or duration of the exposure. For tumours to arise eventually the carcinogen must be administered for a certain minimum time. The *critical point* lies at 5–8 weeks for the agents usually employed to induce liver tumours in rats, but sometimes — as for kidney tumours induced by dimethylnitrosamine or for stomach tumours induced by nitrosomethylurethane (P. N. Magee and R. Schoental[11]) — a single administration of the carcinogen is sufficient. The latent period is related to the life-span of the species studied; thus the average is 16 years for bladder cancer in humans who have suffered exposure to 2-naphthylamine. The term "precancerous" should really be reserved for tissue studied in the latent period *beyond* the critical point and thus destined to give rise to tumours; but the term is loosely used in the present book to include the first few weeks of exposure to the carcinogen.

Largely because of the time and trouble needed to induce

primary tumours, most experimental work on the characterization of tumours has been done with *transplants*, produced originally by inoculating a fragment of a primary tumour into a normal animal, often under the skin, and maintained through successive generations by repeated transfer. The site for the transfer can be deliberately varied, and much research has been done with free-living *ascites* cells derived by intraperitoneal inoculation. Provided that there is no immunological incompatibility — which is most easily avoided by using host animals of the same species and strain (preferably inbred) as for the primary tumour — transplants can be maintained indefinitely. Transplants, in common

TABLE 1. STAGES IN PROGRESSION, AS SHOWN BY THYROTHROPHIC PITUITARY TUMOURS INDUCED BY RADIOTHYROIDECTOMY
(after J. Furth[23])

Stage	GROWTH as reflected by latent or lag period (months)	FUNCTION as reflected by thyrotrophin content (units/mg)
Normal pituitary	–	0·1
Primary dependent tumour	16–10	0·4–0·05
Grafted dependent tumour	8–4	0·2–0·02
Grafted autonomous tumour	3–1	0·01–zero

with autochthonous tumours, profoundly disturb the metabolism of the host animal, as is briefly considered in Chapter 4.

Within the life history of a primary tumour, or with successive transplantations, there may be *progression* in the sense of apparently irreversible changes in nature, adverse to the host — a definition perhaps too loose to meet with universal acceptance. There may, for example, be increased autonomy as shown by loss of functions such as (in the case of liver) bile secretion, by loss of responsiveness to hormonal or other influences which at first could modify the growth of the tumour, or by loss of actual dependence as instanced by certain tumours produced by and initially requiring (for maintained growth) a particular endocrine environment (Table 1). Foulds[21] points out that there are "two main alternative explanations of progression as a mutation in the sense of heritable alterations in the structure of the genome or as durable, replicable changes in the utilization of a structurally invariant genome".

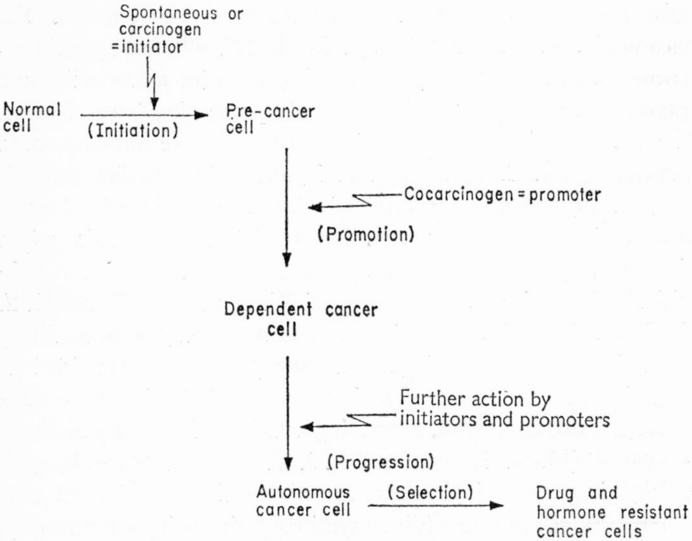

FIG. 1. Stages of cancer development (V. R. Potter[46]). It is envisaged that mutations could occur during both initiation and progression, and that hormones could influence both promotion and progression.

Most authors feel that carcinogenesis is a two- or multi-stage process. Figure 1 gives an appraisal of present-day views on stages in tumour development, as crystallized by (*inter alia*) I. Berenblum[21,32,48], E. V. Cowdry[7], L. Foulds[21,24,32], J. Furth[23], and A. D. Glinos[32]. Various converging lines of study as appraised by V. R. Potter[40] have suggested that, in carcinogenesis, "the initial event is a single-cell phenomenon, that it is irreversible for as long as the cell may live, and that the initiated cell is not yet in a state of autonomous growth . . . " and that carcinogenesis is "a process that consists of a number of *irreversible* steps, some of which can be facilitated by certain biochemical changes that are reversible". Reversibility of the promotion stage would, of course, render the *overall* process reversible up to the critical point mentioned earlier.

This appraisal (cf. Fig. 1) should not be taken to represent universal agreement on stages common to all tumours. The pathologist R. A. Willis (see p. 548 in ref. 49) has questioned whether cancer arises only from a single cell (or a few cells) and whether the concepts "initiation" and "promotion" are of value. The supposed irreversibility of the initial change has also been questioned (H. S. Kaplan[21]). It is uncertain whether there is always a promoter in the form of a known or unidentified agent distinct from the carcinogen. Progression to neoplasia might hinge merely on attainment by the affected cells of a certain critical colony size (I. Berenblum, cf. W. S. Bullough[21] and H. S. Kaplan[21]. Even where there is known to be an exogenous auxiliary agent, it should be realized that "the phenomena classified as cocarcinogenic, in spite of their apparent similarity, may be a heterogeneous collection, expressing a variety of basically different processes" (M. H. Salaman and F. J. C. Roe[11]). For carcinogens which, given as a single dose, are disposed of rapidly yet ultimately produce tumours (dimethylnitrosamine being an example), the postulated promotion must be very rapid if due to the carcinogen, or must be attributed to unknown (endogenous ?) factors.

Some authors (e.g. H. S. Kaplan[21]) use the term *neoplastic transformation* in the narrow sense of initiation; but here it is loosely used to connote the whole chain of events leading to the appearance of a transplantable tumour, not necessarily autonomous in the sense of having lost "dependence".

Histology

To the cancer biochemist, histology serves mainly as a guide to the interpretation of results for a tissue lump that may be far from

Plate 2

Histology of abnormal liver specimens. Magnification ×105.

TOP LEFT:

(a) "Minimum-deviation" hepatoma (actually a 13th generation transplant of the Morris 5123 hepatoma); note double cords of cells separated by prominent vascular spaces, and areas of glandular appearance. (From paper by H. P. Morris and co-workers, 1960[35].)

BOTTOM:

(b) Liver with bile-duct proliferation induced by a non-carcinogenic agent α-naphthylisothiocyanate; note central vein (upper centre) and well-demarcated hepatic lobules, these nodules being normally hard to distinguish.

TOP RIGHT:

(c) Precancerous liver from 5 weeks of azo-dye feeding (this feeding eventually giving rise to nodules as depicted in Plate 1); note heterogeneous appearance, with bile-duct proliferation — compare with 2b — and fat deposition (top), and with signs of fibrosis and necrosis.

a hyperplastic condition may have to be arbitrary, hinging largely on the extent to which the normal tissue organization is lost. Thus, either "hepatomas" or "hyperplastic nodules" may arise in the livers of rats after azo dye feeding (Plate 1). Certain "minimum-deviation" hepatomas (cf. Plate 2a) have close histological affinities to normal liver, yet they are definitely cancerous since they are transplantable.

Particularly for primary tumours (cf. Plate 1) not subjected to transplantation, non-homogeneity presents a serious problem. "So-called 'mush' chemistry involves the breaking up of comparatively large masses of malignant cells, contaminated by the inclusion of variable numbers of normal cells and of some intercellular materials, the separation and collection of fractions of cells and their analysis. This has supplied valuable information; but the individuality of cancer cells is completely submerged . . . " (E. V. Cowdry[7]). With regard to areas of apparently normal tissue within tumour nodules, the problem is unlikely to be serious if the nodule is large, since the very size of the nodule implies a predominance of rapidly dividing cells, cancerous or at least hyperplastic. There remain other problems (cf. Plate 1) such as the presence of intercellular materials (manifest under the microscope as "stroma", "fibrosis" or "cirrhosis"), leucocyte or Kupffer-cell (littoral-cell) infiltrations, lipid inclusions, and apparently dead (necrotic) cells.

The actual tumour-cell areas may vary in general appearance, even in a single animal. Hepatomas may have a gland-like (adenomatous) appearance as shown in Plate 1a, or a cord-like (trabecular) arrangement reminiscent of normal liver, as shown in Plate 1b, or bizarre features such as cysts. Proliferation of bile-duct cells may, if moderate, give a mixed hepatoma-cholangioma or, if predominant, give an actual cholangioma, biochemical comparison of which with normal liver is risky since parenchymal cells comprise, in the rat, about 90% of the weight of the liver and 65% of the cells[41,85]. There is, however, disagreement among morphologists on the cellular origin of primary tumours in the liver[22,41]; thus it has been suggested that parenchymal cells are the source of almost all liver tumours including cholangiomas, or conversely that all hepatomas (or at least adenocarcinomas) as well as cholangiomas arise from bile-duct cells — or perhaps from a supposed stem cell which, in normal differentiation, can give rise to either bile-duct or parenchymal cells.

As is discussed in Chapter 2, biochemists should at least take the precaution of histologically checking any "hepatoma" tissue taken for analysis. Transplantation may be valuable in reducing histological heterogeneity, particularly if the tumour is put through a tissue-culture or ascitic stage (cf. ref. 37). Increasing attention is being paid to transplanted hepatomas of "minimum-deviation" type, so designated because both histologically (Plate 2a) and biochemically they show few major divergencies from normal liver[35]. With transplantation there is, however, the possibility of secondary metabolic changes associated with progression of the tumour (Chapter 8).

Precancerous tissues. Few histologists would venture to pick out particular cells (as distinct from cell masses) as tumour forerunners in a tissue rendered precancerous by carcinogen administration. The guess has been made that hepatomas rise from certain large cells rich in DNA (R. Daoust[1], J. Hoffman *et al.*[108]), but proof is difficult to obtain. According to E. Gläss (cited by Koller[21]), hyperdiploid cells in percancerous liver are not malignant as judged by transplantation behaviour. The proportion of the original cells actually converted into tumour cells may well be low, of the order of hundreds of cells, amongst which only a few might be highly malignant and mainly responsible for the tumour nodule or nodules ultimately observed. Transformation of even a thousand cells out of the many millions present in a tissue would be quite in accord with the view that cancer is a single-cell phenomenon[40]. Given that conclusive evidence on this question is hard to obtain, the possibility that the majority of the cells in a carcinogen-treated tissue become cancerous should be regarded by the biochemist as wishful thinking, although he is entitled to designate the whole tissue mass as "precancerous".

At the outset of carcinogen administration there is often an arrest of cell proliferation (J. M. Vasiliev & V. I. Guelstein, 1963[55]). However, hyperplasia is commonly found at some stage in precancerous tissues, although the proliferative response of epidermis to a promoter (croton oil) given alone may surpass that produced by a carcinogenic hydrocarbon (Carruthers[17]; Green & Savigear[100]). Accompanying or, more commonly, preceding the appearance of hyperplasia there is often histological evidence of cell damage, particularly in the cytoplasm (Plate 2c; note fat deposition). Parenchymal-cell damage and eventual hyperplasia are effects common to different hepatocarcinogens, in so far as common features can be discerned among the diverse histological effects reported from different laboratories even for a single hepatocarcinogen[22]. Damage in the form of necrosis is not invariably a prominent feature of precancerous tissues, nor is hyperplasia always manifest before the critical point (Vasiliev & Guelstein[55]). Eventually precancerous liver may show "foci of regeneration" (cf. Plate 1, c and d), often giving rise to "hyperplastic nodules" which may resemble hepatomas in size and in many biochemical characteristics, and do in fact appear to develop into frank hepatomas[22,41,95,168].

Parenchymal cells in precancerous liver may show nuclear abnormalities, as in hepatomas. Often, but not invariably (cf. R. E. Stowell[16]), there is nuclear enlargement and nucleolar proliferation and enlargement[22], even with thioacetamide[14,188] which usually produces cholangiomas (although Busch[16a] states that it gives hepatomas).

Stich[1] concluded that carcinogenesis hinges on three factors: damage to chromosomes, cell proliferation, and unresponsiveness to stimuli (such as partial hepatectomy) which normally provoke mitosis. It is not clear whether he regards all three factors as operating in any one cell, and indeed parenchymal cells are not distinguished from other cells in his data. Daoust[1], in broad accord with conclusions reached by Stich and earlier authors, considers that hepatomas result from destruction of parenchymal cells offset by formation of new, basophilic cells rich in RNA and

(α-naphthylisothiocyanate) which is not carcinogenic and which is further mentioned in Chapter 7 in connection with the possibility that some "hepatomas" may really have originated from bile-duct cells.

Electron Microscopy

With the improvement of techniques for electron microscopy, new vistas on cell structure have been opened up[13a]. In respect of fine structure, as of biochemical parameters, differences among normal cells of different types are overshadowed by common features which will now be summarized.

Normal cells (Plate 3a). Surrounding the cell there is an apparently double membrane (plasma membrane, cell membrane), which, like most membranes within the cell, probably consists of lipid sandwiched between two layers of protein. In the nuclear membrane there appear to be pores (M. L. Watson[7]) or sieve-like areas (A. Claude[21]), but it does follow that there is no restriction in communication between nucleus and cytoplasm. The inner layer of the mitochondrial membrane is folded to form internal cristae on which respiratory enzymes are located.

In the cytoplasm of most cells there are stacks of paired membranes forming the endoplasmic reticulum (e.r.), each pair enclosing a so-called cisterna. Some of the membranes are smooth-surfaced — sometimes termed γ-cytomembranes, or β-cytomembranes if they comprise invaginations of the plasma membrane — and may, at least in liver, play a role in glycogen storage. Others (α-cytomembranes, ergastoplasm) are rough-surfaced and basophilic by virtue of adhering spherical particles (Palade particles), each 15–20 mμ in diameter. These particles are also found free in the cytoplasm — free particles being common in cells not secreting protein — and within the nucleus (particularly adjoining the membrane; M. L. Watson[7]). They are rich in RNA, and comprise the ribosomes of the biochemist, whereas the complete cytomembrane system is the main component of the microsomal fraction. Cytomembranes appear to have connections both with the cell exterior (P. Emmelot *et al.*[13a]) and with the nucleus, of uncertain importance in the economy of the cell.

Cells also contain some less prominent organelles which cannot readily be isolated free from the above-mentioned elements. The

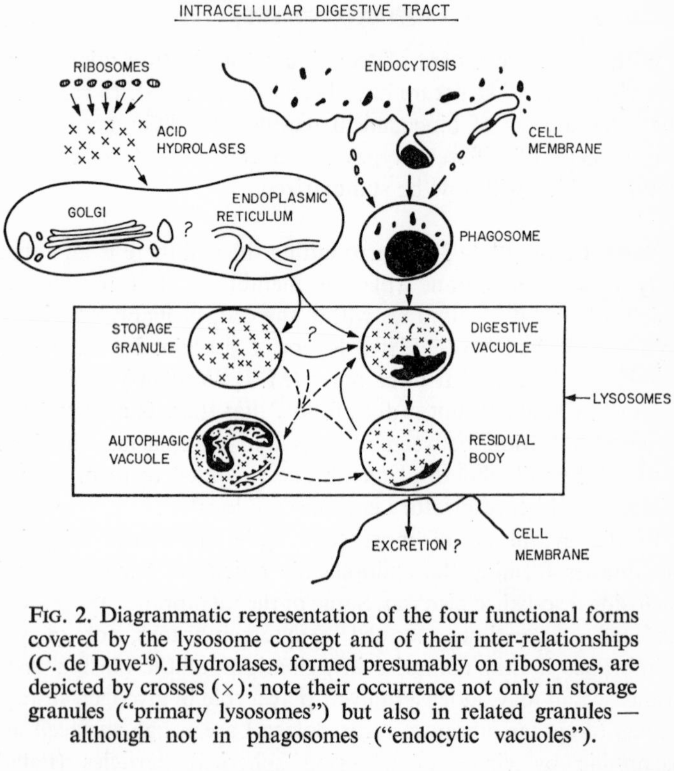

FIG. 2. Diagrammatic representation of the four functional forms covered by the lysosome concept and of their inter-relationships (C. de Duve[19]). Hydrolases, formed presumably on ribosomes, are depicted by crosses (×); note their occurrence not only in storage granules ("primary lysosomes") but also in related granules—although not in phagosomes ("endocytic vacuoles").

Golgi apparatus (A. J. Dalton[7]) is a cluster of smooth-surfaced γ-cytomembranes lying close to the cell border and probably concerned with synthesis, storage, or secretion (to the cell exterior?). Lysosomes are rich in hydrolytic enzymes and were in fact originally defined as particles containing acid phosphatase. They include the "pericanalicular dense bodies" which, as stained with osmium tetroxide, are granular and surrounded by a single membrane; but the concept of lysosomes has now become broadened (Fig. 2; de Duve[19]). Entry of lysosomal enzymes into digestive vacuoles apparently transforms the latter into phagosomes, which transport and catabolize materials arising from the cell exterior; if the materials to be digested are derived from within the cell, the organelles concerned are autophagic vacuoles. Vacuoles in which digestion has been completed may persist in the cell as residual bodies, particularly towards the end of the life span of the cell. So-called micro-bodies or uricosomes, distinct from lysosomes, seem to be the locus of uricase, D-amino acid oxidase and catalase. Among elements peculiar to particular cell types, mention may be made of glycogen granules (liver) and keratin filaments (epidermis).

Tumour and precancerous cells. Tumour cells may show diverse abnormalities in fine structure, the general impression being loss of regularity[12,34,35] (Plate 3, b and c). However, no generalizations are possible, and indeed tumour cells may be indistinguishable from the parent normal cells.

The rough-surfaced cytomembranes typical of cells manufacturing protein for secretion tend to be deficient in the cells of tumours, especially if anaplastic, and free ribosomes tend to be numerous. Mitochondria may show degenerative changes, such as apparent loss of internal structure; counts on mitochondrial fractions do in fact show a reduced number of particles[6,41,45]. However, mitochondria appear normal in some hepatomas (A. J. Dalton[21]). There may be structural aberrations in the nucleus, and enlargement of the nucleolus (W. Bernhard and N. Granboulan[16]). The plasma membrane shows, as in Plate 3b, poor adhesion to those of neighbouring cells (P. Emmelot *et al.*[13a]), as also found by cell physiologists (E. V. Cowdry[7]).

The foregoing changes are evident even in normal cells when the division rate is high, as in embryonic development or repair of injury. Virus particles in tumours (M. A. Epstein; L. Dmochowski[7]) are difficult to identify unequivocally. In certain tumours viruses are undoubtedly present, but it is uncertain whether they are "passengers" or causative agents (R. J. C. Harris[11]). The Golgi apparatus may adjoin the nucleus rather than the plasma membrane in hepatomas lacking the bile-secreting capacity of normal liver (Novikoff[7]), but shows no consistent change in appearance with cancer. No consistent pattern of change has so far been found for lysosomes (Novikoff[7]) or cognate organelles (A. J. Dalton[21]).

Acute (single-dose) treatment with various hepatocarcinogens causes striking enlargement of the smooth-surfaced cytomembranes, often with a rise in the proportion of unattached ribosomes as in tumours[102] and sometimes with evidence of impaired glycogen storage in the cytomembranes (K. R. Porter and C. Bruni, 1959[41]). Such changes persisted throughout the 5 weeks of a chronic experiment, and mitochondria became increasingly structureless and swollen as well as reduced in number; but the nucleus and nucleolus were unaltered[87] (cf. ref. 190). The effect of one non-carcinogenic azo dye (4-dimethylamino-2-methyl-azobenzene) differed little from that of the carcinogenic dyes, except that fragmentation and dispersion of granular lamellae was slower[120]. Indeed, changes like those produced by hepatocarcinogens may likewise occur, reversibly, in situations such as prolonged fasting or exposure to carbon tetrachloride (which, in the rat, injures liver cells but is not carcinogenic); no change specifically linked with carcinogenesis has yet been established (cf. K. R. Rees[19]; W. S. Hartroft[19]). Possibly, however, one effect of carcinogenic azo dyes may be important — an aggregation of certain cytomembranes, suggestive of erroneous hypertrophic regeneration[190].

CHAPTER 2

Approaches to the Cancer Problem

SPACE precludes a historical survey of cancer research. Browsing in other publications (e.g. refs. 24, 40) may be instructive, at least in revealing some false trails and bad experimentation. Tumour work in biochemical papers sometimes appears to have been done as an afterthought, with whatever tumour material happened to be at hand. It is seldom profitable to take short cuts. Careful experimentation can enable much to be learnt about cancer, despite our present-day ignorance concerning the normal processes of cell division. In the attack on the cancer problem, the biochemist occupies a central but not isolated role.

Role of Different Disciplines

Work within and especially between different disciplines is vital to elucidation of cancer. The biochemist should ideally have some familiarity not only with morphology — especially in relation to the tissue samples chosen for study — and with cellular physiology and genetics, but also with fields such as endocrinology, immunology, nutrition, pharmacology (cf. Chapter 9), physical chemistry, radiobiology, and virology (cf. Chapter 3). Influences of endocrine glands and of nutrition on the induction or growth of tumours are touched on later (Chapters 3 and 9), but really fall outside the scope of this book. The list could readily be extended, for example by including environmental statistics and medicine.

Few biochemists can range over such wide horizons of knowledge, even on the experimental as distinct from the clinical side.

In any case, the pressure sometimes put on the non-medical biochemist to go to the cancer patient's bedside and to study human cancer is more often based on emotion than on logic. As a minimum requirement, the biochemist should have enough contact with non-biochemical fields to avoid adding to the pile of bad experiments in the cancer literature. Conversely, workers in non-biochemical fields would often benefit by advice from the biochemist; such advice is all too seldom sought.

Histochemistry and immunochemistry are, strictly speaking, specializations within the broad field of biochemistry, but justice cannot be done here to these powerful approaches. Histochemistry, of which autoradiography may be regarded as a facet, is still mainly a descriptive rather than a quantitative subject, and is notoriously open to artefacts; but its future is bright, and its value in pin-pointing the cell types concerned in biochemical changes is obvious. Some immunochemical findings will be mentioned in Chapter 6, rather tersely in view of the fact that one theory of carcinogenesis is immunochemical in character.

Theories of Carcinogenesis

For the purpose of orientation, the nature of certain theories of cancer will now be indicated, with the warning that the concept of a key step common to all neoplastic transformations should be treated as a hope rather than an assumption.

Prominence has long been given to two metabolic trends in tumours — *high aerobic glycolysis* with impaired respiration (O. Warburg[44]), and a general *convergence* of enzymes towards levels intermediate between the extremes found in various normal tissues (J. P. Greenstein[25]). Most workers now feel that these concepts have outlived their usefulness in the search for key steps in neoplasia.

In the *immunological theory* as advocated by H. N. Green[48,99], changes are postulated in the pattern of antigenic lipoproteins in membranes — both "loss of factors conferring immunological identity on the cells of a tissue" and enrichment in other such factors. This theory, with Green's extension that tumours can produce antibodies to normal host cells, may well be relevant to host-tumour interactions, viz. the restraint of tumour growth by the host, or the invasion of the host by the tumour. However, in the opinion of Sir Macfarlane Burnet[11], "There is no adequate evidence to suggest that immune processes play any positive part in the production of malignant disease . . . (Such theories) are difficult to fit into the general pattern and significance of immune reactions" (see also V. S. Shapot[32]).

For some tumours, the idea of *viral causation* undoubtedly has experimental support (Chapter 3). Extensions of viral theories to accommodate chemical carcinogenesis, hinging on supposed "latent viruses" activated by the carcinogen, must at present be regarded as over-stretched. It is, of course, difficult to distinguish between viral nucleic acids (within the cell) and endogenous nucleic acids.

In discussing "how agents as different as the chemical, physical and viral carcinogens can induce the same biological results . . . ", A. Haddow[32] suggests that "some viruses capable of exerting oncogenic effects do so by direct modification of the genome, with physiological and pathological effects identical with those induced, in some cases at least, by protracted chemical action". Concerning the nature of such a modification, M. Stoker[11] remarks "It is perfectly possible to conceive of a 'hit-and-run' mechanism whereby a virus could permanently alter the hereditary behaviour of a cell after a single brief contact, and with no need for persistence of the virus", but that on the other hand there is evidence of "persistence of integrated genetic material of some . . . tumour viruses".

Addition of new genetic material would, as Potter[40] points out, represent transformation or induction rather than mutation in the usual sense (cf. H. S. Kaplan[21], M. C. Niu[43,54]). Obviously, however, there is no sharp dividing line between viral carcinogenesis by such mechanisms and chemical carcinogenesis entailing *gene modification*. Carcinogens might directly modify DNA itself, in accordance with observations to be mentioned in Chapter 3. Alternatively, carcinogens might bring about an irreversible change in gene expression in more subtle ways, such as will be further considered in Chapter 8.

The emphasis is, at first sight, different in the now classical *deletion hypothesis* of which the main proponents have been the Millers and their colleagues at the University of Wisconsin: " . . . in its simplest form it is intended to mean that a cancer cell lacks some enzyme that is present in the normal cell from which it was derived" (V. R. Potter[8]). At one stage in the development of this hypothesis the emphasis was on deletion in the area of catabolic enzymes. "Catabolic deletion" is now felt, even by its sponsor[40], to have outlived its usefulness as a working concept.

At first sight it is difficult to visualize how deletion of an enzyme — even of an enzyme vital to control of cell proliferation — could lead to the "somatic mutation" which, in some form or other, is thought by A. Haddow and many other workers to underly neoplasia. However, as will be further considered in Chapter 8, there might be early deletions "that will derepress the enzymes associated with DNA synthesis and cell division and thereby produce cancer cells" (Potter[8]) — the term "derepress' implying release of an enzyme-forming system from normal restraints mediated by "feedback" mechanisms. Such "feedback deletion" — a symptom of which might be a *rise* in the amount of the enzyme concerned — could conceivably lead to somatic mutation (at least in the loose sense of a transmissible change in genetic expression) and thence to cancer[39,40]. Such a concept obviously has affinities with the mechanisms mentioned above in connection with viruses[40]. Moreover, the feedback-deletion hypothesis is closely akin to theories in which direct attack by carcinogen on genes is postulated.

There might, then, be alternative ways by which the expression of a given gene could be modified (irrevocably?) so as to trigger off neoplasia. Whatever the nature of a change in gene expression, it is likely to result in, or even arise from, a particular change in cell metabolism, discovery of which should help elucidate the nature of the change in genetic regulatory mechanisms. One such change in metabolism, emphasized in a recent theory[55] may be liberation of lysosomal enzymes into the cell sap. There is, then, a continuing need for classical cancer biochemistry in the sense of the measurement of enzymes and other tissue constitutents, and it is with this theme that the present book is mainly concerned.

Biochemistry and Cancer Research

The search for carcinogens by animal testing[18] or by environmental statistics, and the formulation of theories whereby predictions of carcinogenicity can be made, hardly fall within the scope of biochemistry. It is, however, biochemical techniques that enable products formed from carcinogens in the animal to be identified and their origin explained. An administered carcinogen may well act only after transformation into a particular metabolite; this possibility has an obvious bearing on studies with carcinogens *in vitro*. Such transformations, and chemical interactions between carcinogens or carcinogen metabolites and tissue constituents, are outlined in Chapter 3.

The application to cancer of biochemical pharmacology, as surveyed in Chapter 9, rests on discovery of features in which cancerous cells differ from all the diverse types of normal cell encountered in an organism. However, the survey of metabolic changes in neoplasia which comprises the core of this book (Chapters 4 to 8) has a narrower objective: to compare tumours and precancerous tissues with and only with the actual tissue of origin, in the hope of delineating metabolic changes possibly crucial to neoplasia. As V. R. Potter[8,40] has pointed out, this objective as distinct from a chemotherapeutic objective calls for an approach which has often been lacking in the past merely because of failure to make this distinction. The present emphasis is, then, on phenomena that may elucidate how cancer arises, rather than on cancer biochemistry surveyed from the viewpoint of its possible usefulness to the planning of chemotherapy.

Test Material

In the biochemical study of solid tumours from any aspect, it is customary and advisable to reject any soft material in the centre of the nodule. An outer layer, only a few millimetres thick, may be particularly active metabolically, at least in experiments which depend on uptake of injected materials from the blood (P. Zamecnik[2]; cf. Vasiliev & Guelstein[55]). Often there is an intermediate zone which is not grossly necrotic as judged by its firmness and which is commonly included in samples taken for biochemical examination; but the requisite histological examination may show necrosis of varying extent. It is, however, striking that hepatoma tissue consisting mainly of necrotic cells may show a content of anabolic enzymes and of acid-soluble 5′-ribonucleotides (which are normally in a state of rapid turnover) no lower than that in non-necrotic hepatoma tissue[163]; this situation would hardly be expected in dead or moribund cells. Possibly, then, in the special case of hepatomas and perhaps of other tumours (cf. Table 25 in Aisenberg[6]), necrosis may not invariably connote that the cell is dead. For assessing whether necrosis in tumours implies cell death and how far it distorts the biochemical pattern, tissue autolysis (deliberately induced) as studied in the laboratories of R. E. Stowell[45], C. de Duve[19] and E. Roberts[28] is of dubious applicability as a model.

Among other features of tumour tissue (Chapter 1), fibrosis may be biochemically important: thus, fibrotic hepatomas were notably low in UTP and in conjugated uridine nucleotides[163]. Fibrosis and other complications in precancerous tissues can often be avoided by suitable choice of strain, diet and carcinogen, as will be considered below in the context of hepatocarcinogenesis. In tumours such complications can often be avoided by the use of solid transplants, perhaps passed through an ascitic or tissue-culture stage[37]; the tumours are best studied while still small.

Use of transplants. Transplants are more easily kept constantly available than primary tumours, and if interchanged among different laboratories can serve as standard test material. Repeated transplantation may, however, lead to secondary biochemical changes perhaps associated with tumour progression (Chapter 8). Fortunately, few examples of such changes have so far been reported, and transplanted hepatomas have proved to be very useful test material (see below).

The study of cancer cells in the ascitic form is attended with the difficulty that corresponding normal cells for control purposes are not available in free-living form *in vivo*, and if prepared *in vitro* may be damaged — as shown by leakage of components in the case of liver cell suspensions (P. Emmelot)[13a]. Moreover, the membrane surrounding ascites cells is particularly difficult to rupture, even in the case of ascitic hepatomas[33,117]; recourse must be had to procedures such as ultrasonic disintegration or exposure to a hypotonic medium.

Tumours biochemically comparable with tissue of origin. In choosing test material for study of steps leading to neoplasia, the main limitation is not in obtaining reasonably homogeneous tumour material — difficult though this is — but in finding normal tissue formed predominantly of cells of the type that gave rise to the tumour. This limitation virtually precludes comparisons of, for example, cancerous with normal pituitary glands, and can be quite serious even for the possible comparisons listed in Table 2 (see also Aisenberg's[6] Table 6). Leukaemic leucocytes sometimes, as will become evident, give "out-of-line" results for changes in biochemical parameters, and are perhaps not themselves truly neoplastic (although derived from neoplastic cells); moreover, the heterogeneity of normal leucocytes is a serious pitfall.

To obtain normal mammary gland in adequate amount, recourse may have to be made to pregnant or lactating animals, preferably with a correction for the milk content (A. L. Greenbaum, 1957). There is in fact much to be said for comparing tumours not with "resting" normal tissues, but with tissues undergoing hyperplasia which is not conceivably precancerous in character. Such hyperplasia (often preceded by hypertrophy) can

TABLE 2. SOME TUMOURS POSSIBLY SUITABLE FOR BIOCHEMICAL COMPARISON WITH THE HOMOLOGOUS NORMAL TISSUE

For citations additional to those listed, see [6,18]. The entries are given roughly in order of increasing difficulty in matching the normal tissue with the tumour.

Species	Normal tissue	Tumour	Method of induction, and comments
Rat } Mouse }	Liver	Heptaocarcinoma ("hepatoma")	{ Azo dyes, ethionine, etc. — fed or repeatedly injected[22,41,45]. See text, including Chapter 1 o-Aminoazotoluene or (in old mice of certain strains) spontaneous
Rat, guinea-pig, etc.	Liver, Kidney, lung	Carcinoma (2 types of kidney tumour)	Dimethylnitrosamine, fed in diet (P. N. Magee[11,19])
Hamster	kidney cortex	Carcinoma	Stilboestrol implanted under kidney capsule (V. S. Matthews, H. Kirkman; E. S. Horning)
Rat	Skeletal muscle	Rhabdosarcoma	Local application of Ni or Co Salts, e.g. Ni_3S_2 or CoO (J. P. W. Gilman[31])
Mouse	Lymph nodes	Lymphatic leukaemia	Spontaneous (certain strains); irradiation; methylcholanthrene, given by gastric intubation (D. Burk; J. Victor; P. A. Bianchi[4,60])
Mouse	Thymus	Lymphosarcoma	Irradiation; urethane (H. S. Kaplan[48])
Human	Circulating leukocytes	Leukaemias (not lymphatic)	See (e.g.) W. S. Beck[28], J. R. Bertino[3], F. M. Huennekens *et al.*[16]; but few leukaemic cells proliferate at a neoplastic rate,[4] and homology is difficult to ensure
Human	Uterine endometrium	Carcinoma	See M. L. Dreyfus[6]
Mouse	Epidermis	Squamous-cell carcinoma	Local application of hydrocarbon[17], e.g. dimethylbenzanthracene, often + croton oil. Cf. S. Rogers[8]
Mouse } Rat }	Mammary gland	Adenocarcinoma	{ Spontaneous (certain strains) Methylcholanthrene (C. Huggins[23]) } { Pregnant or lactating animals as "normals"
Rat	Thyroid	Carcinoma	Irradiation, by ^{131}I (J. Furth[23])
Mouse	Lung	Carcinoma	Urethane, given subcutaneously (S. Rogers[117,163]; cf. refs. [64,189]).

be induced in kidney by removal of the opposite kidney, in skin by application of croton oil, and in a liver lobe by removal of the other lobes. So-called regenerating liver is, in Potter's[8] view, the ideal control for hepatomas, the hyperplasia being under tight endogenous restraint. Since, however, partial hepatectomy may in some circumstances accelerate hepatocarcinogenesis[41] (see also A. D. Glinos[32]), certain biochemical changes in a sequence leading to cancer might well occur also in regenerating tissue.

Hepatomas. There is a reasonable likelihood that liver tumours classified as "hepatomas" by histology (Chapter 1) have arisen from the parenchymal cells which comprise the bulk of normal liver tissue. Admittedly there are biochemical differences among parenchymal cells, depending on their position in the liver lobule (e.g. A. B. Novikoff[7,41]). Nevertheless, comparisons between hepatomas and liver are particularly likely to give useful information on steps in carcinogenesis, especially if the material includes "minimum-deviation hepatomas" — so termed because they show few histological or biochemical differences from normal liver (cf. Plates 2a and 3b, Chapter 1) and may even retain the capacity to secrete bile[35]. As will become evident in later chapters, the slower the growth rate of such hepatomas (usually studied as solid transplants) the more closely they tend to resemble normal liver; accordingly, the search for a supposed key step, common to the pathogenesis of all hepatomas, is then less confused by biochemical changes merely incidental to carcinogenesis or associated with *fast* neoplastic growth (V. R. Potter[8]).

The Novikoff hepatoma and, more recently, the Morris 5123 hepatoma have been much studied, the former having very fast growth and the latter still being small even several months after transplantation[45] (but see [200]). Whereas the Novikoff hepatoma is devoid of glucose-6-phosphatase and, as will be shown later (Fig. 10), is high in dCMP aminohydrolase (deaminase), the Morris 5123 hepatoma has an almost normal level of the former enzyme and, like normal liver, shows virtually no activity of the latter[155]. Glucose-6-phosphatase is a "marker" for parenchymal cells, since histochemistry shows it to be confined to these cells in normal liver. Potter[8] may well be correct in suggesting that the Novikoff "hepatoma" really arose from bile-duct cells, but his argument that dCMP aminohydrolase is a "marker" for bile-duct cells has been challenged (see Chapter 7). The fact remains that dCMP aminohydrolase, like glucose-6-phosphatase and certain other enzymes such as glucose-6-phosphate dehydrogenase (high in the Novikoff hepatoma), is a useful criterion in deciding whether a given hepatoma is of minimum deviation type[37].

Minimum deviation hepatomas can be induced, albeit rather unpredictably, by hepatocarcinogens weaker than the commonly used azo dyes, preferably fed intermittently rather than continuously[35]. Primary tumours thus induced have been little studied. Despite the inevitable histological features irrelevant to neoplasia, primary hepatomas warrant study if only because they are less likely than transplants to show biochemical changes associated with tumour progression rather than induction.

Primary hepatomas are most readily induced by feeding with an azo dye, say 0·06% in the diet for 3 months (whereupon the dye feeding can be stopped[41]); they arise between 1 month and 1 year later, the time varying even with "standard" conditions. Tumours arising particularly early should be checked carefully on the suspicion that they may be cholangiomas. The commonly used agent 4-dimethylaminoazobenzene (DAB) is likely to give cholangiomas unless the diet is low in protein; such a diet might, of course, produce biochemical abnormalities even in the controls. The 3′-methyl derivative of DAB is more potent, and even with a high-protein diet — the 20% protein diet developed in A. C. Griffin's laboratory[41] being widely used — it seldom produces cholangiomas. Hepatomas thus produced are fast-growing, but are less extreme than the Novikoff hepatoma with respect to parameters such as glucose-6-phosphatase[163]; the areas of non-necrotic tumour cells may vary in histological appearance, even within a given nodule[37], but only in a few respects[41,163] has a corresponding variation in biochemical pattern been observed. Moreover, comparisons among primary hepatomas induced by different agents (including ethionine[22,37]; see, however, S. Sorof *et al.*, 1963[16a]) have so far disclosed few striking biochemical differences[41]; (cf. ref. 88). There may, however, be fine differences, notably in antigen composition, even among tumours induced in individual animals with the same agent, as shown not only for hepatomas but also, in E. J. Foley's laboratory, for skin tumours (see D. Pressman[1]).

Another type of hepatoma worthy of study is that arising spontaneously (late in the lifespan) in mice of a genetically prone strain. Observations made on this hepatoma in 1943 by F. Dickens and E. Weil Malherbe[6,*129*], to be mentioned later, indicate that a hepatoma warranting the term "minimum deviation" has been available and rather neglected for fully two decades.

Control material for hepatomas (see also Potter[8]). It is essential that the normal liver for control measurements be from animals similar to the hepatoma-bearing animals in respects such as species, strain, and nutritional history. Often there has been neglect of this elementary precaution and sometimes, moreover, comparison of hepatomas only with liver from the hepatoma-bearing animal. The latter practice is unsound, since liver adjoining primary hepatomas has been exposed to the carcinogen and cannot be proved to be normal as distinct from precancerous[41], and since liver from animals with hepatoma transplants is metabolically altered by the latter (Chapter 4).

The possible usefulness of regenerating liver for control purposes has already been indicated, as has the difficulty in choosing controls for ascitic tumours. One possible type of "control" is experimental tissue exposed not to a carcinogen but to treatments such as starvation or hypophysectomy, the aim being to establish the limits of "physiological variation" which a crucial neoplastic change might be expected to surpass[45]. However, with tissues from starved animals, and with embryonic tissue (which is akin to tumours in various biochemical respects, and has often been used as a supplementary control), an unanswerable question arises: might very prolonged starvation or embryonic growth itself lead to neoplasia? Thus the suggestion by G. Weber[46] that lack of xanthine oxidase in tumours can hardly be important, since there is likewise a lack in fasting animals, is a *non sequitur*.

The usefulness of studying animals subjected to dietary or endocrine imbalances lies rather in the delineation of metabolic control mechanisms[46] (cf. Chapter 8), and in the pinpointing of key events in carcinogenesis by choosing treatments that can potentiate or retard carcinogenesis. — "It is reasonable to suppose that treatments which modify hepatocarcinogenesis act by influencing a key step in the latter process, although not necessarily *every* step."[41]

In one respect the study of a spectrum of normal tissues may be helpful, as may be illustrated by glucose-6-phosphatase: the lack of this enzyme in most normal tissues suggests that loss of this enzyme is not a universal step in carcinogenesis, while not itself disproving the possibility that such loss is vital to hepatocarcinogenesis.

Precancerous liver. As will now be discussed in the particular context of liver, precancerous tissues show diverse histological and biochemical changes. The problem is to decide which are relevant to neoplasia. Ideally, as in work with tumours, it is desirable that there should be reasonable homogeneity of cell population, i.e. the experimental tissue should consist predominantly of cells of the type that give rise to the tumour (cf. Table 2). Above all the tissue should be a definite target for the carcinogen in question — a criterion often not met, as for example when methylcholanthrene has been used with liver as the test material[126].

One objection to the study of precancerous tissues is that only a small minority of the cells may give rise to tumours. Since, however, metabolic changes as found in hepatomas are often evident, at least transiently, within 1 month or even 1 week of the start of carcinogen administration[41], it can be argued that most of the parenchymal cells in precancerous liver show changes foreshadowing those in the hepatoma, except of course the supposed cancer-triggering change. In line with the view of I. Berenblum[41] and others that carcinogenesis is a multistage process (Chapter 1), judicious study of precancerous liver can give valuable information on steps in neoplasia: "We may be dealing with a sort of chain reaction, which culminates in malignancy; or with gradual additive modifications . . . " (E. V. Cowdry[7]).

Changes found at 1–2 months are particularly interesting; with much briefer treatment the changes may be ephemeral and merely reflect toxicity of the agent, and in the latent period (beyond two months) the changes may no longer be evident, perhaps because the majority of affected cells undergo biochemical "repair"[41]. In extension of the latter argument, regression of a particular change if carcinogen administration is stopped (beyond the critical point; "reversibility criterion"[41]), does not prove that the change is unimportant, since the change could persist undetected in a few cells destined to become malignant.

Three essential precautions in the study of precancerous tissues should be stressed. Firstly, the animals should be healthy as judged by body weight and food intake; with a robust strain (not necessarily "pure") and an adequate diet, hepatomas can be induced in rats without fatalities (fatality rate 80% in a recent Japanese paper, to be nameless!). Secondly, if actual tumours are not to be studied, it should at least be checked that the carcinogen treatment is such as to lead to the expected tumours. Thirdly, only by the study of different agents, non-carcinogenic as well as carcinogenic, can it be decided which of the observed changes are likely to be "minimum deviations" in the sense indicated above for hepatomas, and which represent irrelevant changes. It may be advantageous to switch from the experimental diet to the control diet on the day before autopsy, thus eliminating effects due merely to "flooding" of the liver with the agent.

With a suitable choice of agent, difficulties caused by tissue-structure changes in precancerous liver (Chapter 1) can be largely obviated[41]. Thus, bile-duct proliferation is not a serious problem with the 4′-fluoro derivative of DAB (although there is an unexplained rise in DNA concentration[163]), nor — in disagreement with other reports[22] — is it extensive with ethionine under the conditions used in the author's laboratory. The latter agents do in fact tend to produce fewer biochemical abnormalities than DAB itself or its 3′-methyl derivative; but a disadvantage of the 4′-fluoro derivative is that it seriously diminishes appetite.

Useful non-carcinogenic agents for control purposes[41] include certain analogues of the carcinogenic azo dyes, α-naphthylisothiocyanate as a trigger to bile-duct proliferation (Plate 2b), and possibly heparin which has been reported to stimulate parenchymal-cell proliferation[215]. To induce cholangiomas deliberately, thioacetamide may be used. Reduction of the admixture of non-parenchymal cells, in rats fed azo dyes, may be achieved by pressing the tissue through a suitable "squeezer"[85]. Ideally, however, biochemical changes occurring supposedly in parenchymal cells should be checked by histochemistry; thus, with this technique it appears that increased abundance of Kupffer cells rich in acid phosphatase and acid ribonuclease complicates the study of these enzymes in precancerous liver.

Baselines for Expressing Results

The practice has grown up in recent years of expressing biochemical results on the basis of cell number, or of DNA taken as a rough measure of cell number. (The DNA content per average cell is high in some tumours including certain hepatomas, but normal or even low in others; see, for example, Kit & Griffin[30], Reid[41], Stich[1], G. Weber[45], M. Weber[202].) The use of cell number or DNA as a basis is justifiable in the case of nuclear constituents, the amount of which could well be independent of cell size, but may actually be misleading in the case of cytoplasmic constituents. If, for example, glucose-6-phosphatase (which is absent from bile-duct cells) were unaffected by hepatocarcinogen treatment, and if there were proliferation of bile-duct cells or other *small* cells such that the number of cells per gram greatly increased but parenchymal cells still predominated on a *weight* basis, the cell basis would falsely suggest an enzyme fall. This argument also applies to tumours, if for example there is leucocyte infiltration. Even if a tumour consisted solely of tumour cells, there is a further argument against the per-cell basis (advanced in the context of hepatoma cells[41]) — that "if they *were* smaller than normal parenchymal cells [which is not necessarily the case] and if each had a normal complement of most cytoplasmic constituents, there would be an absurd lack of room for water".

The author feels, then, that most comparisons of precancerous or cancerous tissue with normal tissue are best made on the classical basis of tissue weight (wet or dry) or of tissue nitrogen (protein), the latter showing a slightly reduced concentration in most tumours[25,41]. Values based on the nitrogen or protein in a sub-cellular fraction, as distinct from whole tissue, are of little use if, as is sometimes the case, no information is given for the yield of the fraction.

Additionally, if only to facilitate comparisons between results from different laboratories, values for cell number or DNA can usefully be included (see refs 41, 199, 202 for examples of changes with hepatocarcinogenesis), together with values for "marker" enzymes as mentioned above in connection with hepatomas. Ideally, biochemical results should be checked histochemically wherever there is reason to suspect an altered pattern of cell population.

Throughout this book, a wet-weight basis is usually implied when changes in tissue composition or metabolism are under discussion — although the basis hardly matters if the change is dramatic.

Delineation of Metabolic Derangements in Cancer

Once the experimental tissue is at hand and the baseline for evaluating results has been chosen, it is a matter of posing questions which are sound and cogent, and of applying standard biochemical techniques to get answers to these questions. A few comments are warranted on questions and on techniques.

Topics worthy of study. With the explosive growth of "molecular biology" (see Fig. 12, Chapter 8) and, in particular, with its extension to mammalian tissues, new experimental vistas are being opened up to cancer biochemists, which as yet have been little explored. As will be evident from Chapter 8, profitable work is possible even with present-day techniques, notably on cytoplasmic topics such as iso-enzymes, control of enzyme activity and functioning of protein synthesis, and on gene expression. Getting to grips with the latter topic will, however, not really be feasible until techniques become available for subtle fractionation of DNA and other nuclear constituents, and until "repressors" can be characterized.

Meanwhile there is still an important place for the more classical approaches which form the main theme of this book. These approaches centre on analyses of tissue constituents and on assays of enzymic activities. Only by judicious choice of enzymes or other constituents can pointers be obtained to fundamental derangements of regulatory mechanisms in neoplasia, as distinct from ancillary changes the interest of which is mainly in connection with pharmacology.

It is a reasonable supposition that metabolic derangements of close relevance to neoplasia will lie at rate-limiting steps. Within a given metabolic area, only some of the steps will be "bottlebecks," perhaps limited by the level of the enzymes concerned, by the availability of substrate (for the use of which there may be competition from other pathways), or by the level of co-factors. No consideration can be given here to this important aspect, to which Sir Hans Krebs and others have devoted much attention.

There are certain pitfalls in the use both of cell-free preparations and also, as will first be considered, of the intact animal — an old-fashioned but valuable test object, more amenable to study now that isotopes are widely available.

Whole-animal experiments. The importance, in relation to human cancer, of appraising derangements in the organism as a whole (cf. Chapter 4) need hardly be stressed. The following comments are restricted to isotopic experiments, the design and analysis of which have been cogently discussed by Zilversmit[50] (cf. ref. 68). Many published observations in the cancer field are of limited value for various reasons. The dose of injected precursor may have been so high that the endogenous pool of the precursor (or of derivatives thereof) was enlarged; the endogenous pool of intermediates as distinct from the end-product may not have been analysed; the precursor chosen may have been rather unspecific for the end-product under study; or the time between isotope

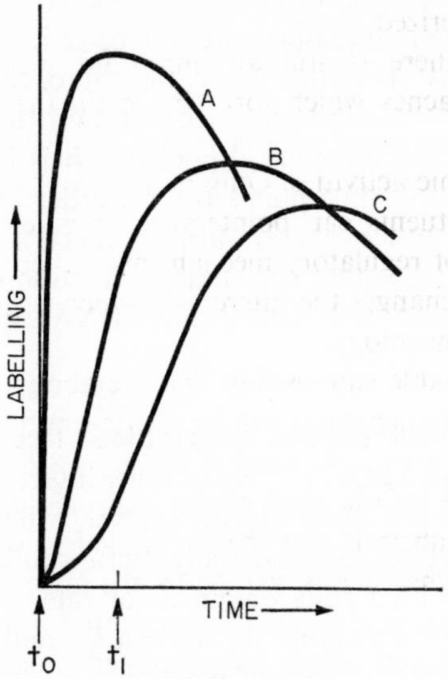

FIG. 3. Schematic curves for *in vivo* labelling (see text for explanation).

injection and killing may have greatly exceeded the time required for the intermediates to attain a peak of specific radioactivity. Given any of these situations, it is impossible to assess whether the endogenous rate of synthesis of the end-product in question was indeed changed in the experimental animals.

An idealized situation may be considered where a precursor *A* is converted into *C* via an intermediate *B* (Fig. 3). Provided that between t_0 and t_1 the specific radioactivity of *B* has not passed its peak (and preferably is still rising linearly), a measure of the rate of synthesis of *C* from *B* can evidently be obtained from comparison of the *amount* of radioactivity in *C* at time t_1 with the *specific* radioactivity of *B* at t_1. A simplified approach such as this is unlikely to give accurate results in practice; but at least, especially if two or more early time points are studied, a rough comparison can be made between experimental and normal tissues with respect to the endogenous rate of synthesis of a particular compound. Even if the tissue in question were to receive its supply of *A* or *B* indirectly, by way of another tissue, the approach would still have some validity. For amino-acid incorporation there may be such fast turnover of the amino-acid pool that it is imperative to get values at very early time points (of the order of seconds rather than hours). A further general warning, concerning the foregoing idealized situation, is that sometimes a fraction of the precursor being incorporated (e.g. uracil into RNA) may bypass the precursor pool[68].

Experiments with cell-free preparations (see also Weber[45]). Work with perfused organs, slices or other intact-cell preparations *in vitro* has a valuable place which, however, will not be discussed. Cell-free preparations give especially useful results, if interpreted in conjunction with results obtained for intact cells and intact animals. Certain difficulties in technique and interpretation, commonly overlooked, warrant mention.

For many enzymic reactions, appropriate supplements must be added (sometimes even in work with "intact" cells), to rectify any dilution or loss of endogenous factors. Thus, with liver mitochondria there is invariably some loss of endogenous cytochrome *c* into the suspending medium. With co-factors and also substrate added in excess, the observed activity should reflect the actual amount of active enzyme, especially if the tissue suspension is so dilute that any endogenous inhibitors are hardly operative. Sometimes, however, it may be advantageous to study a reaction or a complete reaction chain under conditions more closely approaching those prevailing *in vivo*. Here it is preferable to work with a concentrated tissue suspension, and to use concentrations of substrate ("labelled" if necessary) and of co-factors of the same low order as *in vivo*. Where a difference in reaction rate is found between normal tissue and cancerous or precancerous tissue, admixture of the two tissues may be informative in relation to the possibility that an inhibitor or activator in one of the tissues may account for the rate difference (cf. ref. 51).

In the assay of mitochondrial or lysosomal enzymes, it is important that the normal barrier between enzymes and substrate should either be kept as intact as possible, or else deliberately broken. Breakage of uncertain extent, as in homogenates prepared with water or salt solution as medium or with use of a blender, renders the results almost valueless. For lysosomal or other enzymes showing partial latency, the "free" activity which, if the enzyme is soluble, is likely to be recovered in the supernatant fraction may well be a more meaningful parameter than the total activity (cf. Chapter 8, Intracellular compartmentation).

Few authors have been able to isolate lysosomes even in a semi-pure state (C. de Duve[19]). Moreover, many authors have studied preparations of so-called "mitochondria" — or of "nuclei" — which are likely to have been morphologically very impure. Unless good purity is demonstrated, a cautious term such as "nuclear fraction" should be used. This general warning should be kept in mind wherever mention is made later of sub-cellular fractions.

There are now various techniques for isolating nuclei[16] — and even nucleoli[15] — of good purity. At least in the case of liver, nuclei can be regarded as of good biochemical purity if the RNA : DNA ratio is 0·2 or lower, if certain "marker" enzymes — e.g. cytochrome oxidase (mitochondria), acid phosphatase (lysosomes), glucose-6-phosphatase (cytomembranes) and 5′-nucleotidase (plasma membrane) — are virtually absent, and if the capacity for dephosphorylation of UTP is low (G. Siebert, ref. 16 and also joint work with the author). Good purity is, however, incompatible with a quantitative yield of nuclei, and there may be some degree of inadvertent selection as has been shown, by isotopic experiments, in the laboratories of C. P. Barnum (for liver) and of the author (for hepatomas and precancerous liver; M. K. Turner).

CHAPTER 3

Nature of Carcinogens and Interactions with Cell Constituents

SINCE 1775, when the surgeon Sir Percival Pott shrewdly attributed carcinoma of the scrotum in chimney sweeps to soot, a number of carcinogens have been discovered through observations in man. A notable conclusion from the recent application of environmental statistics is that cigarette smoking may lead to lung carcinomas[18,24,27]. The latter phenomenon has not yet been reproduced in animals, although skin tumours have been induced with tarry condensates from the smoke. However, for carcinogenesis by 2-naphthylamine and certain other agents there is quite close parallelism between man and appropriate laboratory animals.

For documentation and extension of the following cursory survey (in which co-carcinogens are neglected), recourse may be had to other publications (e.g. refs. 11, 14, 18, 22, 25, 27, 31, 32, 48) in which more adequate attention is given to the vast literature.

Experimental Induction of Cancer

Cancer can be induced by diverse means, which will now be listed somewhat arbitrarily. No attention can be given here to heterogeneous and ill-defined agents such as pitch, cigarette smoke, rat-liver antisera (which produce hepatomas if prepared against normal, but not precancerous, liver)[99], or (as studied by K. Blomqvist[146]) tissue preparations from regenerating liver.

Questions such as dosage and mode of exposure (cf. Table 2) fall outside the scope of this book. Whereas hepatocarcinogensis by an azo dye given in the diet or by injection may require almost a gram (given over, say, 10 weeks), epidermal carcinogenesis by certain polycyclic hydrocarbons applied locally may be achieved with microgram amounts.

Radiation. X-rays or other penetrating radiations can induce leukaemias or solid tumours; for example, thyroid tumours may arise following massive administration of radio-iodine[23]. Ultra-violet rays may be a contributory cause of melanoma of the skin.

"Mechanical" influences. Tissue irritation or injury by mechanical or other traumatic influences, was long held to be a possible cause of cancer[27], and can at least be implicated as a co-carcinogenic stimulus. Implantation of chemically inert materials such as polythene or stainless steel, particularly in the form of an impermeable film, may produce tumours in adjoining tissues, as demonstrated by the Oppenheimers[18] (see also P. Alexander & E. S. Horning[48], J. M. Vasiliev & V. I. Guelstein[55]). For example, the wrapping of cellophan round one kidney may eventually render it cancerous, by perhaps rendering connective tissue cells anoxic or otherwise damaged, or by "confusing" their normal equilibrium with their neighbours. The lessons from this work have already been passed on to prosthetic surgeons.

Hormonal or dietary imbalances. Tumours of certain endocrine glands may result merely from abolition of hormonal restraining influences[23]. Thus, surgical or "chemical" thyroidectomy may, through abolition of feed-back inhibition of the pituitary by thyroxine, lead to the appearance of pituitary tumours which secrete thyrotrophic hormone. Another means of producing tumours is massive administration of certain hormones, notably the oestrogens (O. Muhlböck & L. M. Boot[48]). The mechanism may, besides a direct action of the hormone on the tissue in question, involve a change in the normal complex equilibrium of hormonal output. Early speculations that steroid hormones are carcinogenic by acting as or giving rise to polycyclic hydrocarbons have become implausible with the advent of stilboestrol and other synthetic hormones which lack condensed rings but may be carcinogenic. Nevertheless, as pointed out by Emmelot[21] (cf. ref. 102), the idea of similarities in mechanism of action between carcinogens and hormones may not be entirely fanciful.

One example of cancer resulting from dietary imbalance is the appearance of hepatomas in consequence of choline deficiency (Le Breton & Moulé[12]). Kwashiorkor, a protein-deficiency disease in humans, is believed by some workers to be a forerunner of primary liver cancer (the latter being a rare disease in humans except, for example, in parts of Africa, China and the East Indies).

In general, hormones and diet are important not so much as actual means of initiating cancer, but rather in modulating the effectiveness of other carcinogenic stimuli — as in chemical hepatocarcinogenesis, for which pituitary and adrenal hormones are requisite (J. H. Weisburger[21]).

Viruses. In the long history of viral carcinogenesis, two notable pioneers were Peyton Rous and J. J. Bittner. Thus, Bittner and colleagues showed that, in mice of suitable genetic and hormonal constitution, mammary cancer arose through a filter-passing factor received in infancy by way of the mother's milk. With the discovery of diverse viral agents (W. R. Bryan[21]), particularly in connexion with avian cancer, there was a tide of enthusiasm for viral theories of cancer causation — a tide which receded, and is now creeping forward again. The polyoma virus, with its remarkable capacity to induce diverse tumours in various species, has attracted particular interest. There is no doubt that certain animal leukaemias have a viral aetiology (I. Berenblum[32], J. Furth[48]).

Viruses from exogenous sources are clearly not primary causes of all tumours, but it has been suggested that activation of endogenous viruses — which can indeed occur after irradiation (H. S. Kaplan[21], R. Latarjet[21]) — underlies cancer other than that produced by deliberately administering viruses. In this connection it is of interest that the production of the anti-virus agent interferon may be suppressed in virus-infected cells exposed to carcinogenic hydrocarbons *in vitro* (E. de Maeyer & J. de Maeyer-Guignard[21]). The possibility that carcinogens activate "latent" viruses (Chapter 1, Theories of carcinogenesis) is hard to prove; even where tumour cells appear in the electron microscope to contain a virus, this might be a "passenger" irrelevant to the causation of the tumour (cf. R. J. C. Harris[11], W. Bernhard[19]). A further possibility is that viruses which themselves are non-carcinogenic may act as cocarcinogens (W. R. Bryan[21], M. H. Salaman and F. J. C. Roe[11]).

The active moiety in the carcinogenic viruses is presumably the nucleic acid, which may be either RNA or DNA. Of interest in this connection are reports (e.g. by S. De Carvalho and by J. Harel; see E. V. Cowdry[7], M. C. Niu[32], V. S. Shapot[32], H. S. Kaplan[48]) — not all fully confirmed — that tumours can be induced by administration of nucleic-acid preparations from tumours or other sources, one example being DNA from certain viruses (e.g. Shope papilloma: Y. Ito and C. A. Evans, 1961).

Chemicals of known structure. The bewildering diversity of chemical carcinogens is evident from the following arbitrarily selected lots, in which references to formulae in Fig. 4 are shown thus [00].

Inorganic compounds: e.g. Be, Cr or Ni, usually administered to the test animals in an insoluble form (free or combined).

Aliphatic compounds: e.g. ethyl carbamate (urethane), thioacetamide (once used in spraying fruit trees!), ethylene imine, dimethylnitrosamine (DMN), ethionine, and — as examples of compounds containing C but no N — lactones such as 2-propiolactone, and carbon tetrachloride (produces liver tumours in the mouse but not the rat). Certain of the foregoing compounds may be regarded as "alkylating agents"[42]. Carcinogenicity is likewise a

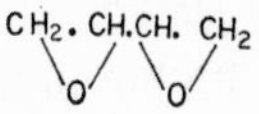

I

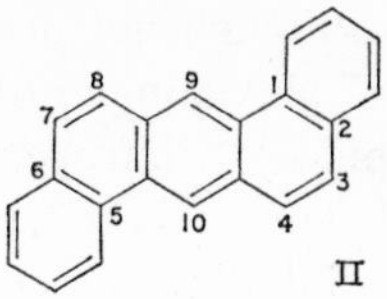

II

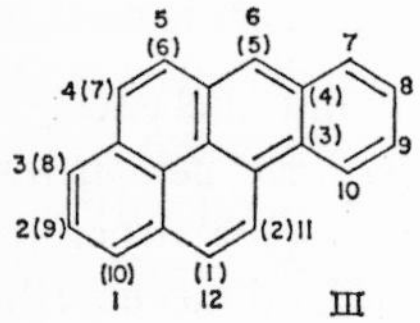

III

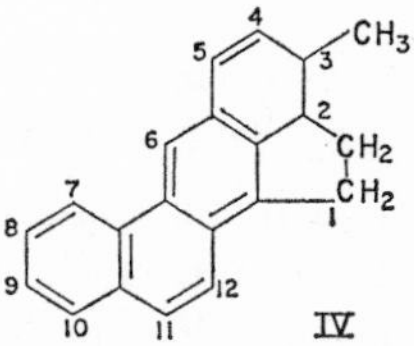

IV

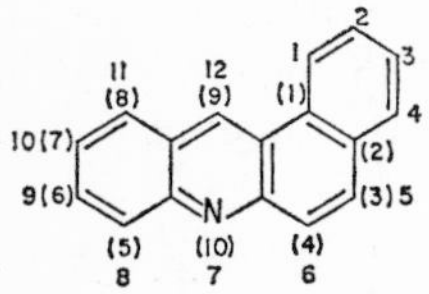

V

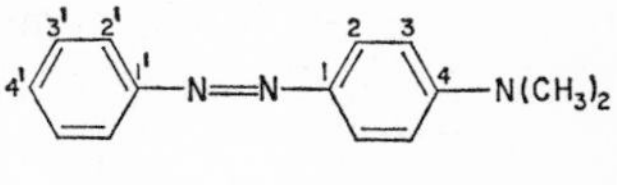

VI

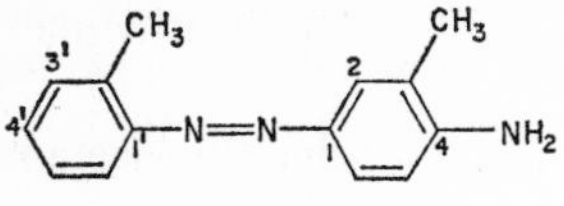

VII

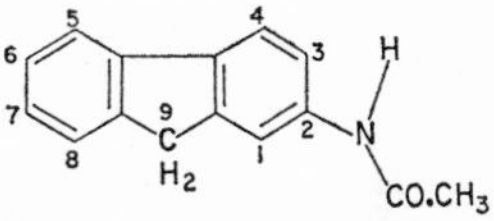

VIII

FIG. 4. Structures of certain carcinogens, II–V are drawn so as to show the structual relationship to cholanthrene. (Names in parentheses are still widely used, but may not conform to present-day nomenclature even in respect of the ring numbering now shown.)

- I 1,2 : 3,4-diepoxybutane.
- II dibenz[*a-h*]anthracene (1,2 : 5,6-dibenzanthracene).
- III benzo[*a*]pyrene (3,4-benzpyrene). Ring numbering in parentheses refers to the parent compound, pyrene.
- IV 3-methylcholanthrene (20-methylcholanthrene).
- V benz[*a*]acridine (1,2-benzacridine). Ring numbering in parentheses refers to the parent compound, acridine.
- VI *N,N*-dimethyl-*p*-phenylazoaniline (4-dimethylaminoazobenzene).
- VII 4-amino-2′,3-dimethylphenylazobenzene (*o*-aminoazotoluene).
- VIII *N*-2-fluorenylacetamide (2-acetylaminofluorene, 2-acetamidofluorene).

property, although not dominant or well documented, of more "orthodox" alkylating agents such as mustard gas (2,2′-dichloroethyl sulphide), "nitrogen mustards" — e.g. *N,N*-di(2-chloroethyl)methylamine (HN2), myleran (synonymous with busulphan; 1,4-butanediol dimethanesulphonate, $CH_3 \cdot SO_2 \cdot O \cdot (CH_2)_4 \cdot O \cdot SO_2 \cdot CH_3$), and epoxides — e.g. 1,2 : 3,4-diepoxybutane [I].

Aromatic compounds, now divided arbitrarily into 3 classes:

Polycyclic (fused-ring) hydrocarbons and aza derivatives, usually active in microgram doses and having some structural resemblance to phenanthrene: e.g. dibenz[*a–h*]anthracene (the first chemical carcinogen to be discovered — E. L. Kennaway, 1929) [II], 7,12-dimethyl-benz[*a*]anthracene (9,10-dimethyl-1,2-benzanthracene in old nomenclature), benzo[*a*]pyrene (present in pitch and in diesel-engine exhaust fumes) [III], 3-methylcholanthrene [IV], and benz[*a*]acridine [V].

N-substituted aminoazobenzenes (azo dyes): e.g. *N,N*-dimethyl-*p*-phenylazoaniline (DAB, "butter yellow"; once used to colour margarine!) [VI], and 4-amino-2′,3-dimethylphenylazobenzene (AAT) [VII].

Amines other than azo dyes: e.g. *N*-2-fluorenylacetamide (AAF) [VIII], 2-naphthylamine, and 4-aminostilbene.

Specificity in Target and in Structure

Some of the above agents, notably the polycyclic hydrocarbons, normally produce tumours (sometimes sarcomas) only at the site of application — although methylcholanthrene given systemically can produce breast carcinomas in rats (C. Huggins[23]). However, dimethylnitrosamine (P. N. Magee[11,19]), urethane[64] and various other agents produce tumours usually at remote sites, which are characteristic for a given agent and for a given species and are sometimes further determined by the mode of administration. Even the strain of animal can be important, as with acetylaminofluorene (AAF), a multi-site carcinogen the targets for which include the liver, mammary glands, intestinal mucosa and middle-ear ducts (E. K. Weisburger & J. H. Weisburger, 1958[41]).

For each of the diverse examples of chemical carcinogens mentioned above, there is a quite specific relationship between structure and carcinogenicity, although certain variations in structure can be tolerated. Thus, in contrast with 1,2:5,6-dibenzanthracene, 1,2:3,4-dibenzanthracene is virtually inactive. In the 2-acetylaminofluorene series the acetyl group is not essential for activity, and indeed even 2-nitrofluorene has some activity; but 4-acetylaminofluorene is inactive (E. K. Weisburger and J. H. Weisburger, 1958[41]).

Among the azo dyes as studied by J. A. Miller and E. C. Miller, certain fluoro derivatives of DAB (e.g. 4′-, 2-, or 2′,4′-) are highly active whereas the 2,6-difluoro derivative is inactive; the 3′-methyl derivative (4-dimethylamino-3′-methyl-azobenzene) is highly active (and is particularly useful for inducing hepatomas, Chapter 2), whereas the 2-methyl derivative is non-carcinogenic (and, surprisingly, *increases* the population of mitochondria[120]). Activity persists if the amino group has only one methyl substituent but disappears if the amino group is unsubstituted. Where, as in many cytotoxic alkylating agents (cf. below), there is a chain of —CH_2— groups, there is an optimum chain length for activity[42].

Molecular properties in relation to carcinogenesis. For individual classes of carcinogens, much effort has been devoted to attempted correlation of degree of carcinogenicity with general properties of the molecule. The results have hardly been commensurate with the effort expended, largely because (as Hieger[27] points out) theoretical chemists have tended to disregard the inaccuracy of most estimates of carcinogenicity.

For the polycyclic hydrocarbons, as studied particularly by the Pullmanns in Paris, emphasis has been placed on the need for a favourable "K region" (or regions) concerned in a hypothetical combination of the carcinogen with an unspecified tissue component; if this region has a high electron density, the activation energy for the supposed combination would be low. Figure 5 shows for benz[*a*]anthracene not only the "K region" but also the "L region" which, as further stipulated, should be of low reactivity. Also specified is an "M region", a site (not necessarily the only site) of metabolic transformation of the molecule *in vivo* — which emphasises that account must be taken of the possibility of such transformation, perhaps into an intermediate which is the true carcinogen. Electronic theories such as that outlined may at least have some value for predicting whether a given compound could be (as distinct from will be) carcinogenic[18].

As E. C. and J. A. Miller pointed out in 1955[41], there are structural affinities between the aminobiphenyls, aminostilbenes and aminofluorenes. For these and other aromatic carcinogens, including the polycyclic hydrocarbons and azo dyes, the general-

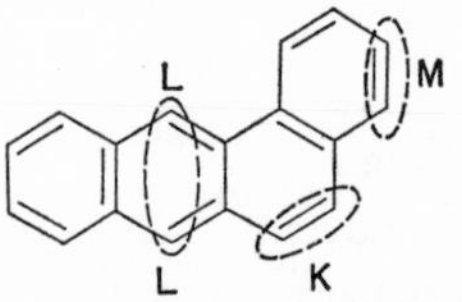

FIG. 5. "K", "L" and "M" regions in benz[*a*]anthracene.

ization may be made that a planar structure of the molecule favours carcinogenicity, but is not an absolute requisite: thus, 9,10-dimethyl-1,2-benzanthracene is non-planar but carcinogenic.

In the context of the aminofluorenes, it has been pointed out by the Weisburgers[41] that "the size and orientation have an important bearing on the carcinogenic properties of a molecular arrangement. This in turn implies . . . that the carcinogenic process is elicited by the combination of the actual carcinogen with an endogenous body constituent under well-defined and stringent electrochemical conditions". As will become evident later in this Chapter, progress is only now being made with delineation of the carcinogen-tissue constituent interactions which, justifiably, have been invoked in the various attempts to explain why carcinogenicity demands particular structures. E. Boyland's suggestion that the importance of planarity may lie in permitting insertion of the molecule into the DNA double-helix has yet to be substantiated.

From evidence which cannot be surveyed here, but is hardly conclusive, Neish[146] has postulated that "carcinogenic activity should be looked for in substances which possess some or all of the following properties: (i) antirheumatic or anti-inflammatory activity. (ii) metal ion complexing ability. (iii) ability to produce a rise in the soluble thiol components (e.g. GSH) of tissues. (iv) ability to bind to tissue constituents."

Alkylation capacity in relation to carcinogenesis. The structure of many carcinogens is such that they could be regarded as "alkylating agents", sometimes capable of alkylation even at neutral pH values as prevail in the living cell[42] (see also Magee[19]). It would in fact be foolish to expect a single mechanism common to all chemical carcinogens. Theories based on alkylation and applied with discrimination represent a valuable approach which need not invalidate other approaches.

The classical alkylating agents such as mustard gas are notable for two biological properties which may go hand-in-hand with carcinogenicity: mutagenicity and cytotoxicity. The latter property may underly the inhibition of body growth commonly observed in carcinogen-treated animals (J. M. Vasiliev & V. I. Guelstein[55]), and has been exploited with some success in chemotherapy (Chapter 9). Carcinogenicity is in fact overshadowed by these other properties, which have led to the designation "radiomimetic" even though the parallelism with irradiation is not exact. The cell damage with these agents apparently occurs in the nucleus during interphase (whereas X-irradiation seems to act particularly in late prophase) and becomes manifest during mitosis, accumulating with successive mitotic divisions until the cell dies or becomes malignant. In the broader context of 'somatic mutation' theories of carcinogenesis, F. M. Burnet[18] remarks: "the words mutagen and carcinogen should be synonymous". However, reservations are necessary; thus for certain mutagens (e.g. formaldehyde, nitrous acid, caffeine) carcinogenicity has yet to be demonstrated.

The biological activity of alkylating agents was once believed to be virtually confined to bi-functional as distinct from mono-functional compounds. R. J. Goldacre, A. Loveless and W. C. J. Ross[42] suggested in 1949 that the biological activity may be due to a bridging action, between or within chromosomes or possibly proteins or other long-chain molecules. As an alternative explanation of the action of alkylating agents (such as epoxides), and also of azo dyes and aminostilbenes, J. A. Hendry & collaborators[18] postulated formation of intracellular polymers, through interaction with non-polar side-chains in proteins or nucleoproteins with resulting micelle formation; but A. Haddow has pointed out that such polymers could not be formed by primary alkyl methane-sulphonates such as myleran.

In view of recent observations that certain monofunctional alkylating agents are biologically active[18], it now appears likely that activity depends only on alterations in *individual* target molecules, perhaps DNA molecules (see end of this chapter). The actual reaction mechanism underlying the alkylation, as discussed by G. P. Warwick[3], may be either of the Sn1 type as for mustard gas, or of an Sn2 type for agents such as epoxides, β-lactones and myleran.

Cross-linking or other dual effects can hardly be attributed to carcinogens such as dimethylnitrosamine, but single-point alkylation — perhaps by a metabolite — is plausible and, for some carcinogens, substantiated (see below). It is possible but unlikely that carcinogens which are not actual or potential alkylating agents can trigger off an alkylation process by endogenous cell constituents — an idea recently developed by P. R. Srinivasan and E. Borek. Probably alkylation is one of several alternative actions that can lead to a secondary effect or effects centered on mechanisms controlling cell division (Chapter 8).

Metabolic Transformations of Carcinogens

Almost without exception, foreign compounds become chemically modified in the body and particularly in the liver, often by oxidation and ultimate conversion into glucuronides (glucosiduronates) or other "detoxication" products through the action of microsomal enzymes. Because of the complexity of metabolic transformations, attempts to delineate specific sites of carcinogen localization — within the cell or at least within particular tissues — have so far given rather disappointing results. Examples will now be given of metabolic transformations, some representing disposal mechanisms and others perhaps representing essential steps in carcinogenesis.

Dimethylnitrosamine (as studied particularly by P. Emmelot and by P. N. Magee[11,19]) appears to owe its carcinogenic activity to formation of carbonium ions (CH_3^+) or, more probably, diazomethane (itself a carcinogen; chemists beware!), via a highly unstable intermediate:

$$(CH_3)_2N.NO. \xrightarrow{N\text{-demethylase}} [CH_3.NH.NO] + HCHO$$

$$[CH_3.NH.NO] \swarrow CH_3.NH_2 \qquad \searrow CH_2N_2 \text{ (diazomethane).}$$

For *alkylating agents* such as nitrogen mustards, there is likewise evidence of the formation, at least *in vitro*, of unstable (cationic) intermediates, as discussed by Warwick[3].

Urethane is metabolized to the *N*-hydroxy derivative, itself carcinogenic and capable of alkylation; in the liver there may be formation of *S*-ethyl glutathione, and urinary derivatives include ethyl mercapturate.[64]

Ethionine appears to be metabolized to *S*-adenosylethionine, but it is uncertain whether this intermediate is responsible for the observed ethylation of nucleic acids[22,187]. It has been suggested that importance of this intermediate lies in its depriving the cell of adenine nucleotides — the administration of adenine being a means of blocking certain actions of ethionine[91].

Polycyclic hydrocarbons, to which E. Boyland and his associates[11] have given particular attention, commonly give rise ultimately to glucuronides. Some hydrocarbons (although not benzpyrene) also yield mercapturates (through reaction with glutathione) or etheral sulphates. There appears to be initial formation of epoxides involving adjoining ring carbons, for example in the "M region" (Fig. 5). Alternatively, there can be initial formation of monohydroxy derivatives as by addition of water across double bonds. Ultimate products, excreted largely as glucuronides or sulphates, include monophenols, diols, and diphenols derived from the diols. The excretion occurs largely in urine but partly in bile.

As an example of the complexities encountered, 1,2:5,6-dibenzanthracene (studied in C. Heidelberger's laboratory) showed some hydroxylation in the "K region" and gave 5-hydroxy-1,2-naphthalic acid (non-carcinogenic) as one ultimate product. Greenstein[25] has rightly emphasized that the various transformations so far demonstrated affect only a very small proportion of the administered hydrocarbon, and that their significance for carcinogenseis is uncertain.

Compounds such as 2-*naphthylamine*, as studied particularly in the laboratories of E. Boyland[9,48] and of G. M. Bonser[48] and D. B. Clayson[11,18], give rise to phenols as for the hydrocarbons. Thus, 2-naphthylamine yields 2-amino-1-naphthol which, after conversion into its glucoronide in the liver, can be again liberated in the bladder through the action of β-glucuronidase and can give rise to bladder tumours. Boyland and co-workers have further shown that 3-hydroxyanthranilic acid, a metabolite of tryptophan, can induce tumours when implanted into the bladder — although there is no reason to believe that dietary tryptophan is a hazard.

Clayson[18] has suggested that any aromatic base with two or more rings is likely to be carcinogenic if it is readily converted *in vivo* into an *o*-hydroxyamine and if the latter is not present solely in a conjugated form. He is rightly cautious in advancing this hypothesis, and its revision may be needed in view of the *N*-hydroxylation recently shown for certain amines, as mentioned below.

As summarized by the Weisburgers[41], 2-*acetylaminofluorene* resembles the hydrocarbons in undergoing hydroxylation (at positions 3, 5 and 7 as well as 1), and also can be reversibly deacetylated. The hydroxylated intermediates are excreted as glucuronides and sulphates. If, however, the carcinogenic activity is due to an intermediate, this is unlikely to be the 1-hydroxy derivative — important though this is for the protein-binding to be mentioned below — but might be the N-hydroxyl derivative[111], the formation of which has been demonstrated in the Millers' laboratory[18].

The metabolic transformations of 4-*dimethylaminoazobenzene*, to which the Millers[41] have devoted much attention, include reduction of the azo linkage (—N=N → —NH—NH—), the product being non-carcinogenic. There is little evidence of ring hydroxylation, but an early and possibly important metabolic change is reversible demethylation (with release of HCHO) to give the monomethylamino derivative, itself carcinogenic, which subsequently may be irreversibly demethylated to the non-carcinogenic primary amine. The demethylation proceeds via a hydroxymethyl intermediate (>N—CH_2OH).

Closer consideration cannot be given here to the wide topic of metabolic transformations of carcinogens, or to the enzymic mechanisms concerned. As will be briefly considered in Chapter 4, azo dye feeding itself affects the levels of microsomal enzymes concerned in the metabolism of azo dyes, but it is unlikely that such changes in enzymic activity are requisite for carcinogenesis. The possibility that a particular metabolic transformation may be necessary to render a "carcinogen" carcinogenic must be kept in mind in attempts to demonstrate *in vitro* effects on tissue metabolism, and in studies of interactions with tissue constituents.

Reactivity of Carcinogens towards Tissue Constituents

Carcinogens have generally shown a disappointing lack of selectivity in their intracellular localization. The agent, or a metabolite indistinguishable from it with the test used, is typically found in each of the fractions obtained by differential centrifugation from the target tissue. However, carcinogenic hydrocarbons (and also anthracene) were associated largely with "microsomal" and supernatant fractions prepared from skin, and also from liver and kidney[70]. Moreover, hepatocarcinogenic azo dyes show some predilection for the supernatant fraction and also, as stressed by S. Fiala[41], for the microsomal fraction — particularly the "smooth-surfaced" component (R. W. Baldwin & C. R. Barker[21]), as may also be the case for dimethylnitrosamine (P. N. Magee & T. Hultin[11]). Microsomal contamination might account for the dye found in "nuclear" and "mitochondrial" fractions; but purified nuclei await study. Azo dyes have yet to be studied in relation to the observation[55] that carcinogenic hydrocarbons as detected by fluorescence microscopy are concentrated in lysosomes in tissues such as skin. One difficulty in interpreting azo-dye results is that initially the non-parenchymal cells seem to take up more dye than parenchymal cells[85].

Studies with carcinogens *in vivo*. Results for diverse carcinogens, restricted to observations on target tissues, are summarized in Table 3 (see also P. N. Maggee[21]). Evidently both proteins and nucleic acids may take up, at least to a small extent, the carcinogen or the carcinogen skeleton, or may become modified through alkylation by the carcinogen. The classical observation of firm binding of azo-dyes or azo-dye metabolites to protein still awaits delineation of the chemical nature of the binding. Alkylation of certain amino acids has, however, been demonstrated with dimethylnitrosamine (Table 3). Whereas agents such as ethionine and dimethylnitrosamine alter nucleic acids *in vivo* by an alkylation process, dimethylaminoazobenzene and possibly acetylaminofluorene form an acid-labile linkage, apparently missed in early studies in which phenol was not used to isolate the nucleic acids.

Interactions between carcinogens and tissue constituents are evidently of diverse types, and it remains to be seen which interaction is important for a given carcinogen, and what is the genetic consequence of a given type of interaction (cf. Chapter 8). Here it should be emphasized that binding to nucleic acids is very small in magnitude, of the order of 1 molecule per DNA molecule in the case of dimethylbenzanthracene[67] (cf. Magee[19], Goldner *et al.*[97]).

Studies with carcinogens *in vitro*. Evidence concerning binding of carcinogens *in vitro* warrants mention, despite its uncertain relevance to *in vivo* behaviour as pointed out by D. B. Clayson[18] and by H. G. Mandel (see Magee[19]). Observations in E. Boyland's laboratory, although at one stage criticized by C. Heidelberger[39], suggest that carcinogenic hydrocarbons can interact with DNA, apparently at "loosely ordered helical regions"[63]. With photoradiation in a wavelength range corresponding to the absorption band of 3,4-benzpyrene, the latter apparently becomes covalently linked to DNA in the "coil" form (P.O.P. Ts'o & P. Lu, 1964[63]).

Liver-slice experiments in T. Hultin's laboratory[18,131] have indicated that monomethylaminoazobenzene, aminofluorene or dimethylnitrosamine may become bound to microsomal membranes under oxidative conditions. For the binding of acetylaminofluorene to proteins *in vitro*, prior deacetylation and 1-hydroxylation seem to be obligatory[143], although the resulting intermediate is non-carcinogenic. *In vitro* binding of azo dyes as studied in the Millers' laboratory[18] was shown to differ in character from that demonstrable *in vivo*. Non-enzymic binding to nucleic acids (as distinct from protein) was found by J. J. Roberts and G. P. Warwick[3,165] with 4-hydroxymethylaminoazobenzene, which may arise from the dimethylamino compound *in vivo* and mediate its carcinogenic action. The observed linkage to DNA and RNA was of an acid-labile character, apparently involving the formation of cyclic derivatives of cytosine and guanine.

Roberts and Warwick[3] had previously studied alkylating agents *in vitro*, and *in vivo* with particular attention to urinary constituents, and found that the —SH group of cysteine (either free or in peptide linkage) was chemically modified, apparently through a sulphonium intermediate. With myleran (busulphan) the target sulphur atom was actually eliminated, and with mustard gas or aromatic nitrogen mustards there was cross-linking between sulphur atoms. Warwick[4] emphasizes that firm conclusions concerning the mechanism of action of alkylating agents on cells cannot be drawn from such observations, or from observations of attack on nucleic acids as found with bifunctional alkylating

TABLE 3. TARGET-TISSUE CONSTITUENTS AFFECTED *in vivo* BY CARCINOGENS (BINDING OR CHEMICAL MODIFICATION)

Single doses were commonly used for the work cited, although only with repeated doses would tumours have arisen in liver or skin.

Carcinogen and tissue	Constituent affected	Specificity in relation to carcinogenesis	Authors
4-Dimethyl-aminoazobenzene (DAB) and other azo dyes; liver	Protein (all cell fractions, but notably "slow h_2" proteins in supernatant — Chapter 6); bound dye resists organic solvents, etc. Little bound dye in nucleic-acid fractions — but possibly missed[165]. Some binding to serum albumin (J. Dijkstra)	Liver-protein binding quite specific, from work with different dyes (2-Me-DAB an exception ?) and species	J. A. & E. C. Miller, S. Sorof (cf. S. Fiala *et al.*)[41]; J. M. Whitcutt[204]
DAB; liver	Cytoplasmic RNA: merely C transfer from Me group by "formate pathway", with no purine methylation		M. Berenbom (see Magee[19])
DAB; liver	RNA (isolated by phenol procedure): concentration of label (from ring-C) almost as high as in protein	Low binding with aniline or in hepatoma-resistant strain of rat	F. Marroquin & E. Farber[22]
DAB; liver	RNA, DNA (phenol procedure). Degree of binding: protein>RNA >DNA	Little binding to spleen RNA	J. J. Roberts & G. P. Warwick[165]
Acetylaminofluorene; liver	RNA (phenol procedure); concentration of label (from 9-C of ring) almost as high as in protein, but label not in usual nucleotides after hydrolysis		F. Marroquin & E. Farber[22]

Ethionine; liver	DNA and especially RNA: probably ethylation of purines. Also some incorporation into proteins		E. Farber[22]; P. N. Magee[10,19,21]; J. A. Stekol[187]
Dimethylnitrosamine and analogues; liver, kidney and lung	Proteins, DNA and RNA: alkylation, mainly of guanine (at 7 position, as shown with RNA). Protein alkylation — as also shown with slices *in vitro* (Magee & Hultin[10]) — appears to be on histidine and (less) on —SH of cysteine; perhaps on microsomal-membrane protein	tert-Butylmethyl-nitrosamine (inactive?) gave no 7-Me-guanine. Low RNA alkylation in non-target organs	E. Farber[22]; P. N. Magee[10,19,21] Z. M. Craddock[79]; P. Emmelot
Benzpyrene, dibenzanthracene; skin	Protein (all cell fractions, but "microsomal-fraction" binding perhaps especially important)	No protein binding in liver, etc. (after skin painting). Non-carcinogenic hydrocarbons bind similarly, except to "nuclear" fraction	E. C. Miller; G. Calcutt[71]; cf. S. Fiala[41]
Hydrocarbons, e.g. dibenzanthracene; skin	DNA, RNA and protein (a particular electrophoretic component). Binding to DNA not proved to be "tight"	Protein binding (Heidelberger) or DNA binding possibly correlated with carcinogenicity	C. Heidelberger & G. R. Davenport[67] (cf. ref. [48]); P. Brookes & P. D. Lawley[67]
Tri*cyclo*quinazoline; skin	"Within the limits of detection [it] is not strongly bound to any skin component"		R. W. Baldwin[55]
Nickel carbonyl; lung	Binding of Ni to RNA fraction precipitable by NaCl	Similar binding in liver (not a target)	F. W. Sunderman[189]

agents[194] — one effect of which is cross-linking between guanyl residues in the wide angle of the DNA helix (Fig. 6).

The salient feature of alkylation of nucleic acids is formation of 7-alkylguanine (as first shown by P. D. Lawley & C. Wallick[8]), possibly preceded (in P. Alexander's opinion) by attack on

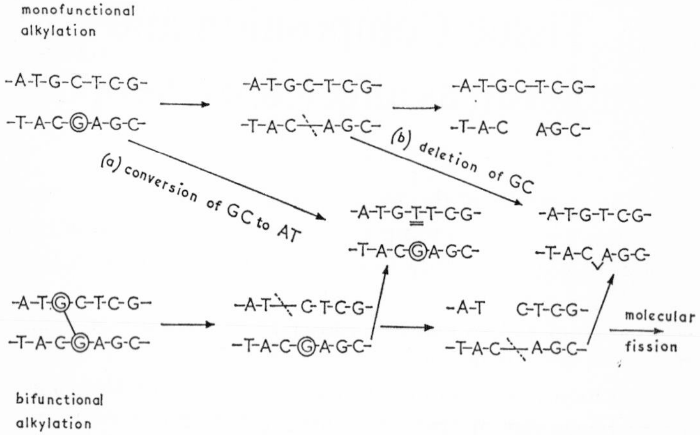

FIG. 6. Alkylation of DNA by monofunctional and bifunctional alkylating agents, and subsequent effects of alkylation (P. Brookes & P. D. Lawley[11]). Base sequence along DNA molecular chains is represented by initial letters of bases. Horizontal arrows show effects of hydrolysis of alkylated DNA. Inclined arrows show possible mechanisms for mutagenesis initiated by faulty replication of the lower DNA strand.

phosphate residues to give an unstable intermediate which rearranges. The diverse effects of alkylating agents on nucleic acids, as summarized in Fig. 6 (P. Brookes & P. D. Lawley[11,16]), have been shown *in vivo* as well as *in vitro*, but not with tissues which are definitely targets for carcinogenic as distinct from cytotoxic actions of the agents — a limitation which also applies to the above observations on —SH groups.

CHAPTER 4

Tissue Composition and Metabolism as affected by Neoplasia

THE main emphasis of this book is on the search for key changes in precancerous and cancerous tissues. Firstly, however, brief consideration will be given to effects of tumours on other tissues in the "host" animal.

No attempt will be made to consider the literature on changes in "non-target" tissues or body fluids during the actual course of carcinogenesis. One example is a fall in blood caeruloplasmin (a copper-containing enzyme) following acute treatment with hepato-carcinogens (Neish, 1958[146]). The topic has been studied especially by certain Japanese authors[41] (e.g. K. Ashikawa, G. Doi, K. Haruno, S. Ichii).

The Tumour-bearing Host

The presence of a tumour, primary or transplanted, markedly influences the metabolism of the host[14,20,25] (cf. ref. 32). Effects thus produced in the host are obviously of clinical importance in relation to diagnosis and to care of the cancer patient, and may also be an experimental pitfall — many biochemists having injudiciously used host liver as the "control" tissue for primary or transplanted hepatomas. The liver adjoining primary hepatomas has, of course, been exposed to the action of the carcinogen, and is in fact "precancerous" at least with respect to some biochemical parameters[41].

There may be reciprocity in tumour-host tissue interactions, the growth or metabolism of the tumour being itself modified by the host, as already touched on (Chapter 1) in the narrower context of tumour "dependence". Immunological interactions may be particularly important, for example in governing the viability of metastases (see below). However, attention will here be confined to the host animal as affected by the tumour.

Abnormal constituents in the blood or urine of tumour-bearing animals (see below) commonly originate from the tumour itself. Changes in other tissues might be produced indirectly, perhaps by an alteration in endocrine balance; thus, host animals may show stress-like changes in adrenocortical secretion, with a phase of adrenocortical exhaustion. Another indirect mechanism, perhaps hardly capable of accounting for the selectivity of some of the effects, is protein deficiency in the host due to "nitrogen trapping" by the tumour (cf. Chapter 6). Some effects, however, may be due to a direct action on the tissue of agents produced by the tumour itself, notably "toxohormone".

Toxohormone. In 1948, W. Nakahara & F. Fukoka[14] reported that a product isolated from tumours and designated "toxohormone" caused, when, injected into animals, a striking depression of liver catalase (an enzyme which is low in the livers of tumour-bearing animals). Toxohormone conceivably plays a role in the cachexia observed in cancer patients, but has yet to be fully characterized. It has some protein-like properties, being soluble in water and precipitable by agents such as trichloracetic acid, but unlike most proteins it is thermostable. There is some evidence that the agent can be extracted not only from tumours but also, albeit less readily, from normal tissues. In general, the role of the agent in mediating tumour effects on host metabolism is far from clear.

The latter conclusion also holds for the supposed "malignolipin", which could be isolated from human tumours but apparently not from normal tissues, and which was thought to consist of a spermine-containing phospholipid (T. Kosaki and co-workers[9,14]);

it could be detected in the blood as well as in the tumour (see Le Breton & Moulé[12]). These observations have yet to be confirmed[16a]. "Oncotrephin", isolated from hepatomas, is said to stimulate the growth of cancer-cell cultures and the incorporation of orotate into RNA[209] (see also M. Kuru & G. Kosaki[32]). Tumours and host tissues are said to be rich in "carcinolipin", an agent that stimulates amino-acid activation (Hradec[32]).

Abnormalities in host organs. Changes attributable to the presence of a transplanted tumour include rises in the content of nucleic acids, for example in kidney and lung (L. R. Cerecedo[207]), and in the RNA/DNA ratio in muscle [207].Most attention has been devoted to the liver; here the changes include an apparent rise in the rate of nucleic-acid synthesis[25]. Other changes in liver include increased activity of alanine-α-oxoglutarate transaminase (C. A. Nichol & F. Rosen[3,46]) and xanthine oxidase[207], decreases in NAD-pyrophosphorylase[188] and tryptophan pyrrolase (Y. Yamamura *et al.*[32]), altered activities of enzymes concerned in carbohydrate metabolism[201], and increased activity of "latent" alkaline ribonuclease as measured after destruction of the endogenous inhibitor[169].

Blood and urinary constituents, and relevance to diagnosis. The presence of a tumour can lead to diverse changes in blood composition, such as a fall in albumin and a striking rise in certain mucoproteins[14,16a]. In one type of leukaemia, multiple myeloma, there appear abnormal γ-globulin components, differing from one patient to another, and the urine contains "Bence-Jones proteins". In perfusion experiments precancerous liver has shown changes in plasma-protein output, the pattern depending on the hepatocarcinogen[69].

Much work has been done on blood enzymes[16a,20]. With carcinoma of the prostate, studies by A. B. Gutman & E. B. Gutman in 1938[30], followed up by W. H. Fishman and others, showed a markedly increased content in serum of an acid phosphatase in which even the normal prostate is rich. Serum alkaline phosphatase activity, to which O. Bodansky has given special attention, is increased with skeletal cancer and, less strikingly, with myeloid leukaemia. Among enzymes which may show increased activity with cancer are glutamate-α-oxalacetate transaminase (H. M. Dyer *et al.*, 1961[88]), lactate dehydrogenase and aldolase.[6] The extra aldolase in the blood of rats bearing a primary hepatoma is of an "embryonic" type[178] — an observation which reflects the increasing attention being paid to isoenzymes in cancer.

Histamine is one example of a urinary constituent which rises with cancer, at least in animals bearing certain transplants[164]; but the rise is slight in the early states of tumour growth, as also found for the rise in allantoin and uric acid[207]. Biochemical changes may be found in secretions other than urine; thus, with uterine cancer there may be increased levels of β-glucuronidase and of 6-phosphogluconate dehydrogenase in vaginal fluid.

Hopes have repeatedly been raised that a particular component of blood or other body fluids would be of clinical value as a pointer to the presence of cancer, but so far this approach has led to few applications — mainly because a change in level seldom occurs at an early stage of tumour growth and, moreover, may occur in disease states other than cancer. Already, however, certain tests have proved of value for specific types of cancer, such as prostatic tumours.

Metastases. The tendency for primary tumours to metastasize calls for biochemical study, with attention to the host as well as to the tumour itself. One difficulty in the biochemical study of metastases is that the animal may die before enough material is available. As early as 1925, J. B. Murphy & J. A. Hawkins[6] reported that the respiratory and glycolytic capacities of spontaneous tumours in mice showed no correlation with their tendency to metastasize. Catalase activity was reported by Matsumoto and co-workers in 1960[41] to be less depressed in hepatoma metastases than in the primary hepatoma — a difference which might be due to superior histological uniformity of metastases. Surprisingly, the metastatic spread of mammary tumours in mice was enhanced by orotate administration, the mechanism being unknown[77].

The molecular events which lead a primary tumour to metastasize may well not be intracellular, but reflect changes with malignancy in the cell surface, as summarized by P. Emmelot *et al.*[13a]. Malignant cells, in common with some proliferating normal cells, show impaired contact with adjoining cells, perhaps because of loss of antigens[99] or of Ca^{2+} ions[114] and other constituents requisite for adhesion (D. R. Coman[*114*], E. V. Cowdry[7], G. Klein[21]), or because of an enhanced negative charge (J. M. Vasiliev & V. I. Guelstein[*55*]; cf. below, Sialic acid). Biochemical study of such parameters has become feasible now that techniques are available for isolating plasma membrane fractions from liver and hepatomas (P. Emmelot *et al.*[13a]).

Tumours and Precancerous Tissues: Areas of Study

As was discussed in Chapter 2, elucidation of steps leading to neoplasia hinges on judicious study of tissue composition and metabolism, with particular attention to homology of cell type. Information on a given metabolic process should, ideally, comprise data for enzyme activities, for the levels of substrates and intermediates, and for the rate of the process in the whole tissue or whole animal; moreover, following lines of thought to be indicated in Chapter 8, it may be advantageous to have information on "metabolic adaptation" to dietary or other exogenous influences. For few metabolic areas has this ideal build-up of information been approached.

Rate-limiting steps are particularly likely to repay study (Chapter 2), even if a direct relationship between the step in question and the rate of cell division is not obvious. The data to be surveyed are not, however, restricted to such steps; indeed it is often difficult to decide whether a particular step is in fact rate-limiting in the normal tissue or at least potentially rate-limiting in tumour tissue.

In anticipation of the observations to be discussed, it may be pointed out that for many parameters neoplasia may entail a rise, rather than "deletion" or "convergence" as emphasized in early theories (Chapter 2).

In the large metabolic areas centered on carbohydrate, protein and nucleic acid, the literature is correspondingly large, and will be considered in Chapters 5–7. Coenzymes will be mentioned in Chapter 5. Lipids will be considered later in the present chapter, except for fatty acid metabolism which is surveyed in Chapter 5.

Various Tissues Constituent (other than enzymes)

Data for the levels of lipids, carbohydrates, proteins and nucleic acids will be given elsewhere, as just indicated. Certain other non-enzymic constituents warrant brief mention, although few of these are conceivably crucial to the malignant transformation and few have been studied in "minimum-deviation" tumours. Where mention is made of abnormalities in precancerous liver with a particular carcinogen, other agents either were not tested or else indicated a poor correlation with carcinogenicity.

Inorganic constituents. The study of inorganic anions has so far given little rewarding information (K. B. Olson *et al.*[32]). Cations such as Ca^{2+} and Mg^{2+} have been studied in situations such as hepatocarcinogenesis[41,129] and epidermal carcinogenesis[17]; the fall in Ca^{2+} in the latter situation seems to be a characteristic of benign hyperplasia rather than neoplasia. With azo-dye feeding, nuclear fractions from liver have shown depletion of Na^{+}, K^{+}, and especially of Ca^{2+} and Mg^{2+} [65]; since the fractions were presumably contaminated with plasma-membrane fragments, one locus of the fall in Ca^{2+} might well have been the membranes. (Hepatomas, however, may be less prone than liver to have increased membrane permeability when treated *in vitro* with EDTA[114]). The level of Cu^{2+} may be high in hepatomas and somewhat low in precancerous liver (G. Doi[41], M. Arnold and D. Basse[65]). Microsomal fractions from Morris 5123 hepatomas are somewhat low in Mn^{2+} and in "Fe_x" (haem-protein ?[145]).

These and other studies[25] have hardly established any dramatic and consistent abnormalities, with neoplasia, in the levels of cations. However, valuable pointers to loci concerned in the neoplastic transformation might emerge from closer study of trace metals necessary for the activity of particular enzymes[9] or, conceivably, for the integrity of nucleic-acid structures[189]. Further work on cation levels should also help in evaluating hypotheses centering on metal chelation (A. Furth and other authors[65,146]), and in elucidating the possible importance of changes in ion-transport systems (cf. J. D. Judah *et al.*[19]).

Vitamins. Mention will be made elsewhere of certain vitamins in connection with their function as coenzymes. To summarize observations made with hepatomas[9,25,41], there are reports of depletion of Vitamins A and B_{12}, biotin, niacin, panthothenate, pyridoxine, thiamin and tocopherols but not of ascorbate. Some depletion in precancerous liver has been noted for B_{12} (V. Mitbander *et al.*[161]), pyridoxine and riboflavin; but only for riboflavin is there some evidence of a correlation with the carcinogenicity of the agent[41]. Apparent increases in ascorbate synthesis (see E. Boyland[21]) are of dubious relevance to carcinogenesis. Hepatocarcinogenesis entails little change in the intracellular distribution of riboflavin or other vitamins.

Sialic acid (*N*-acetylneuraminic acid), a membrane constituent which appears to be largely responsible for the high negative charge of cancer cells but which is not essential for the life of the cell, is somewhat high in leukaemic leucocytes, particularly in myeloid leukaemia[149]. Its level in solid hepatomas (as distinct from ascitic hepatomas, for which G. T. Fuhrman *et al.* gave data in 1962) may be considerably increased, and its composition and its sensitivity to neuraminidase may be altered[113]. The increase was, however, small for the Morris 5123 hepatoma, particularly if the transplants were intramuscular rather than intraperitoneal

(H. Kalant, M. Guttman & H. P. Morris, unpublished). Recent analyses on isolated plasma-membrane fragments for sialic acid (P. Emmelot *et al.*[13a]) leave open the possibility that its content is increased in hepatomas.

Various Enzymes

Like the foregoing survey of tissue constituents, the present cursory survey refers to enzymes not dealt with elsewhere and seldom shown to rank as possible loci for the malignant transformation. Other authors[20,25] have made fuller surveys, not restricted to comparisons with homologous normal tissues.

Catalase has long been a focus of interest, although its normal role is by no means clear. The activity is low in many tumours and also in the liver of tumour-bearing animals[25], but in the case of hepatomas[35,41] the fall in activity is not invariably marked and thus can hardly be a "minimum deviation". It has rightly been pointed out that there is a need for more subtle investigation, for example in relation to possible endogenous inhibitors[9].

Phosphatases. The literature on "ATPase" is hard to interpret, largely because of lack of appreciation by some experimenters of the partial latency of ATPase activity, of its dependence on the choice of activating cation, and of its diverse and complex functions (e.g. in oxidative phosphorylation and in ion transport) as studied in the laboratories of P. Emmelot[13a], L. Ernster and A. Lehninger (*inter alia*) and as reflected by its occurrence in different particulate elements of the cell, The total activity assayed in the presence of Mg^{2+} ions is sometimes but not invariably low in hepatomas, and a fall in mitochondrial-fraction activity may be accompanied by an apparent shift into the nuclear (crude) and microsomal fractions (C. Allard and collaborators, 1957[41]). Nuclear and microsomal fractions warrant closer study, with strict attention to their morphological purity. "Free" ATPase in mitochondrial fractions may be high in hepatomas relative to total ATPase[41], but this observation does not itself prove that the integrity of mitochondria is impaired.

The dephosphorylation of triphosphates other than ATP deserves study, particularly in view of results with UTP (Chapter 7). Nucleoside diphosphates seem not to have been tried as substrates in biochemical studies on carcinogenesis. The dephosphorylation of nucleoside-5′-monophosphates, due mainly to a 5′-nucleotidase which requires Mg^{2+}, is mentioned in Chapter 7 in the context of UMP metabolism; the activity of plasma-membrane fractions was high for a hepatoma compared with liver (Emmelot *et al.*[13a]), but histochemistry shows that the high activity resides in fibrotic areas rather than in the plasma membrane (Novikoff[7]; A. A. El-Aaser, unpublished).

Non-specific alkaline and acid phosphatases have been widely studied, usually with β-glycerophosphate as substrate. Their normal role in metabolism is rather obscure, and their levels are usually not dramatically changed in tumours or in precancerous liver. Alkaline phosphatase activity, however, may be elevated in hepatomas and also in regenerating liver, especially if assayed in the absence of Mg^{2+} ions (e.g. C. Allard *et al.* 1957[41]). Nuclear fractions (crude) normally show high activity which, however, is not selectively affected by hepatocarcinogenesis and which, from comparison of different normal tissues, is uncorrelated with mitotic rate. However, in plasma-membrane fragments from a hepatoma notably high activity has been found (Emmelot *et al.*[13a]). For leukaemic leucocytes there is a report of low activity of alkaline phosphatase (E. Salvidio *et al.*[4]).

The "total" activity of acid phosphatases may be low in the livers of rats fed azo-dyes — carcinogenic or non-carcinogenic — but near normal in certain hepatomas[41]. The supernatant-fraction activity, a measure of the "free" activity, may be elevated in hepatomas and particularly in precancerous liver[41], but less dramatically than that of another lysosomal enzyme, acid ribonuclease (Chapter 7). The high acid-phosphatase activity found in cancerous prostate is due to an enzyme which, unlike acid phosphatases such as that of liver, is not inhibited by tartrate. Different enzymes or isoenzymes may have contributed to acid- or alkaline-phosphatase activity as studied in some laboratories, particularly where phenyl-phosphate or *p*-nitrophenyl phosphate was used as substrate (cf. ref. 139).

Other hydrolases. The total activity of β-glucuronidase — which is largely located in lysosomes — was increased in epidermal carcinomas studied by P. U. Angeletti *et al.*[139], and in various tumours studied by W. H. Fishman and others[20,25]. Hepato-carcinogenesis, however, entails little change in activity[41]. Acylase and esterase activities, assayed with various substrates, are low in some tumours, but the decreases are hardly notable in extent or consistency[25,35,41,114], except perhaps in the plasma membrane (Emmelot *et al.*[13a]; see also Novikoff[7]).

Drug metabolism and some catabolic reactions. Glucuronide formation will be considered in Chapter 7. Various hepatomas have shown a fall in *N*-demethylase and reductase activities with azo-dye substrates (cf. Chapter 3; A. H. Conney & J. J. Burns[46], J. R. Fouts[46]). Although a fall is also evident in regenerating liver, the possibility remains open that a "minimum deviation" will be found in this microsomal area.

A depression in rhodanase activity has been observed in primary hepatomas and, transiently, in precancerous liver (D. M. Greenberg and co-workers, O. Rosenthal[41]). Low activity of "cystine desulphurase" as found in some hepatomas[25] may, as suggested by J. A. Stekol and co-authors in 1958 (see Le Breton & Moulé[12]), be a reflection of deficiency of $NADH_2$ and of pyridoxal phosphate, which participate respectively in the reduction of cystine to cysteine and in the splitting of the C—S bond in cysteine.

Various authors[113,119,164] have studied the decarboxylase which converts 5-hydroxytryptophan into serotonin but which is also active (at pH 8) towards dihydroxyphenylalanine and histidine. In precancerous liver there is a fall in activity, possibly specific (Kizer, 1963[118]), but hepatomas do not invariably show low activity[35]. The fall in monoamine oxidase activity (commonly assayed with serotonin as substrate) seems to be non-specific[35,41].

Some synthetic reactions. Low activities have been observed for UDPglucose-UDPgalactose epimerase in mammary carcinomas compared with lactating mammary gland[167], and for glyoxalase in leukaemic leucocytes[128]. Accelerated formation of glucosamine has been reported for primary or Novikoff hepatomas (D. E. Kizer[41,45]). Precancerous liver shows a reduced capacity for taurocholate formation[175].

Lipid Levels and Phospholipid Metabolism

The content of neutral fat in tissues is, of course, normally very dependent on nutritional and endocrine status. Determinations on tumours, as summarized by Le Breton & Moulé[12] and, rather inaccurately, by Haven and Bloor[26], have sometimes shown low values but hardly suggest a pattern specific for malignancy. The fatty acids in hepatomas are similar in type to those in liver (P. H. Figard & D. M. Greenberg, 1962[74]).

There is little biochemical evidence bearing on speculations by H. N. Green (Chapter 2) that neoplasia may hinge on changes, perhaps structural, in certain phospholipids supposedly located in membranes and important immunologically. Undoubtedly, however, phospholipids are coming to the forefront in connection with membranous structures and with processes such as electron transfer (S. Fleischer) and protein synthesis[38], and might well be concerned in cancer.

With epidermal carcinogenesis, an increased level of phospholipid (and of lipid choline and inositol) is found in the carcinomas although not in hyperplastic tissue, but there is little change in phospholipid composition[17,74]. With hepatocarcinogenesis, however, there is eventually a fall in phospholipid content, particularly in the supernatant fraction; even the Morris 5123 hepatoma showed a fall, but there was little change in phospholipid composition other than a rise in cephalin at the expense of lecithin

(P. W. Figard & D. M. Greenberg, 1962[74]; for other work on hepatocarcinogenesis see refs. 26, 41, 45 and 74). H. H. Williams and co-workers stated in 1945[26] that the phospholipid concentration is low in nuclear preparations from azo-dye hepatomas, but their data need re-investigation in the light of values published in 1951 by A. C. Griffin and collaborators[30] and of the crudity of the preparations.

Phospholipid synthesis. Nuclear-fraction phospholipid as studied in Griffin's laboratory[30] showed, with hepatocarcinogenesis, a rise not only in amount, but also in uptake of injected inorganic phosphate. However, whole-tissue phospholipids in hepatomas or precancerous liver show phosphate incorporation around or (Novikoff hepatoma[45]) below the normal rate[41,109]. Experiments with slices have suggested a slight depression in incorporation with hepatomas[206], but no difference between malignant and benign ovarian tumours from humans[159].

Among hepatomas assayed for the microsomal methylation step whereby phosphatidylaminoethanol is converted into phosphatidylcholine, only the Morris 5123 hepatoma had activity exceeding one-tenth that of normal liver (Figard & Greenberg[74]). In connection with the possibility that the supply of 2-aminoethanol (ethanolamine) may be limiting *in vivo*, it may be pointed out that the level of ethanolamine phosphate (phosphoethanolamine) was low in lymphosarcomas studied by S. Kit in 1953[30], but high in liver after azo-dye injection[146].

In the Novikoff hepatoma there is an accumulation of dCDPcholine, attributable to impaired conversion of the latter into lecithin — there being little change in the capacity for synthesis of dCDPcholine; on the other hand, regenerating liver tends to have an increased capacity for synthesis of lecithin and particularly of dCDP[179]. The findings for the Novikoff hepatoma await extension to other hepatomas; they appear to accord with the abovementioned fall in lecithin content, but it appears that the rat (unlike the chick) makes use of CDPcholine rather than dCDPcholine as a lecithin precursor. A speculation that tumours are low in CDPcholine[33] has yet to be tested.

Choline catabolism. Hepatomas and precancerous liver show a marked fall in choline oxidase activity, possibly an important step in the genesis of fast-growing hepatomas[41]. The fall is, however, small in the case of slow-growing hepatomas such as the Morris 5123[37]. Low oxidase activity, together with high cholinesterase activity as found in some hepatomas[41], would evidently help in the provision of choline for phospholipid synthesis.

Cholesterol is re-attracting interest, following early observations of a dramatically increased level of esterified cholesterol in precancerous liver and hepatomas[41,211]. Free cholesterol may be little changed in the tissue as a whole — for example in mice given the hepatocarcinogen 3,4:5,6-dibenzcarbazole (Boyland *et al.*, 1938[146]) — but very low in hepatoma nuclear fractions as analysed by H. H. Williams and collaborators (cf. p. 68).[26] In Morris 5123 hepatomas there are reduced levels of free cholesterol (in whole tissue) and especially of esterified cholesterol; yet there may be increased incorporation of injected acetate into cholesterol (A. B. Novikoff[7]). Slices from fast-growing hepatomas have shown no marked change in the conversion of labelled precursors into cholesterol (Chapter 5, Fatty acid metabolism).

There is a need for closer investigation of free and esterified cholesterol, with particular regard to rates of formation and of catabolism and utilization. It should be taken into account that conversion of β-hydroxy-β-methylglutaryl-CoA (formed from acetyl-CoA) into aceto-acetate rather than cholesterol (the latter pathway needing $NADPH_2$) would be favoured by decreases in NADP reductase (as may occur in hepatomas[41]). It appears that in tumours the normal inhibition of cholesterol synthesis by dietary cholesterol may not operate (Siperstein[40,47]).

CHAPTER 5

Carbohydrate and Fatty Acid Metabolism

IN normal tissues the inter-relationships between the different pathways of energy metabolism are highly complex and, moreover, show shifts in balance depending, for example, on diet. The latter aspect in relation to tumours will be touched on later (Chapter 8); in the present Chapter it is sought to discuss, with reference to animals on a normal diet and with avoidance of details as given elsewhere (e.g. ref. 6), what generalizations can be made about tumours as compared with homologous normal tissues.

At the outset it may be pointed out that tumours in general[177], and hepatomas in particular (T. Fujii & T. Ushnishi[41], J. T. Nodes & E. Reid[163], *inter alia*), are not invariably very deficient in "energy-rich phosphate" or in nucleotides concerned in metabolic regulation — this view being based on analyses for ADP and ATP, and also for GDP and GTP the functions of which include a role in the oxidation of α-oxoglutarate to succinate (see also ref. 107). For precancerous liver the same generalization applies; thus the ATP content is seldom below half of normal.

Catabolism of Carbohydrate via Pyruvate: Early Observations

The classical view that the energy supply of tumours comes predominantly from glycolysis (even in the presence of oxygen), rather than from respiration, was based on tissue-slice experiments made by O. Warburg[6]. The view received support in 1925 from observations made *in vivo* by C. F. & G. T. Cori (see ref. 2), and from measurements made by J. B. Murphy & J. A. Hawkins[6] on spontaneous tumours, the respiration and glycolysis of which showed no correlation with growth rate. In agreement with this view, the pH of tumours tends to be low *in vivo*[112], presumably because of accumulation of lactate as shown for primary hepatomas by G. A. LePage in 1948[6,41] and recently confirmed[142]. Here it may be noted that lactate dehydrogenase, assayed in cell-free preparations, usually shows activity of the normal order in tumours[6], for example in hepatomas[25] and in leukaemias (leucocyte activity; J. R. Bertino[3]). There might, however, be alterations in enzyme properties, as shown in a chromatographic comparison of a rhabdosarcoma with muscle[139].

Challenges to Warburg's views. O. Warburg has long maintained that impairment of the respiratory system is an early and essential event in carcinogensis, and underlies the increased glycolysis. This view has been heatedly challenged. The extreme counter-view is that there is no impairment of respiratory capacity, the high glycolysis usually observed being due to inadequate blood supply and consequent lack of oxygen. The main difficulty in appraising the evidence is to integrate not only enzymic results obtained by the diverse techniques surveyed in Chapter 2, but also analytical results for the endogenous substrates and co-factors of relevance to the enzymic results.

The conclusion that high aerobic glycolysis is a characteristic of malignant rather than of benign tumours emerged from observations published by M. L. Dreyfus in 1940 for human uterine endometrium[6], and by F. Dickens & H. Weil-Malherbe in 1943 for hepatomas (including spontaneous benign hepatomas in CBA mice)[6,*129*].

However, even in 1951, when the situation was summarized by four U.S. workers — V. R. Potter, R. E. Olson, S. Weinhouse & P. C. Zamecnik[2] — there was still no serious challenge to Warburg's then 30-year-old observation that tumours characteristically have high aerobic and anaerobic glycolysis *in vitro* and a small

Pasteur effect. Moreover, evidence accumulated which seemed to support Warburg's view that respiration is defective: thus the activities of enzymes such as aconitase, succinate dehydrogenase, cytochrome c reductases, and cytochrome oxidase were shown to be low in azo-dye hepatomas as compared with normal liver, as were the levels of cytochrome *c*, FAD, NAD (but see below), and CoA[2,25,41].

This evidence in support of a defect in respiratory capacity was offset by certain other observations. Precancerous liver obtained by azo-dye feeding does not consistently show decreases in respiratory oxidases or an increase in the rate of glycloysis *in vitro*[6,41]. Succinoxidase was found to be normal in hepatomas induced by acetylaminofluorene (C. Hoch-Ligeti), and histochemical study of hepatomas low in succinate dehydrogenase later indicated that many of the hepatoma cells had normal activity (Pearson & Defendi[45]). C. Carruthers & V. Suntzeff[17] showed as early as 1947 that succinoxidase and cytochrome oxidase are even lower in normal epidermis than in epidermal carcinomas induced by methylcholanthrene, with little difference in cytochrome *c* level.

Analyses for citrate (J. A. Miller & C. Carruthers, 1950[17]) on these epidermal carcinomas, on rhabdosarcomas, and on hepatomas indicated a "convergence" rather than a consistent change in citrate level; the epidermal carcinomas had a level below that in the corresponding normal tissue (the level in normal epidermis being high). In V. R. Potter's laboratory a high level of citrate was observed in primary hepatomas compared with liver, and in a transplanted (Jensen) sarcoma compared with muscle. Mere determinations of citrate level are of ambiguous interpretation; but with the advent of isotopic techniques it was shown that tumour slices may oxidize pyruvate or lactate quite efficiently (and also acetate, according to Weinhouse & Olson but not Potter)[2]. Weinhouse found that the level of the condensing enzyme which converts acetyl-CoA into citrate was actually higher in a hepatoma than in liver. In Potter's laboratory, tumour homogenates supplemented with fluoride, to suppress the otherwise excessive breakdown of ATP, showed a good rate of pyruvate oxidation, now limited by the levels of oxidizing enzymes — these enzymes not being rate-limiting in normal tissues. Following

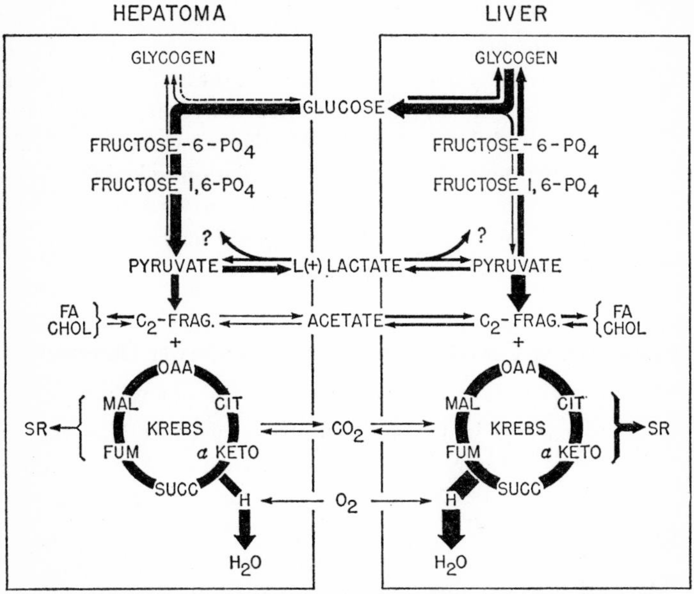

FIG. 7. Differences in carbohydrate metabolism between liver and hepatomas (not "minimum-deviation"), as summarized in 1951 by R. E. Olson[2]. Each box represents a cell, with a blood vessel in the space between them. The thickness of the lines represents the approximate reaction rates. OAA = oxalacetate, CIT = citrate, a-KETO = a-oxoglutarate, SUCC = succinate, FUM = fumarate, MAL = malate, FA = fatty acids, CHOL = cholesterol, SR = side reactions.

injection of fluoroacetate, no accumulation of citrate was demonstrable in tumours although it was sometimes demonstrable in normal tissues.

Situation as assessed in 1951. From work with slices and homogenates, Olson[2] made a perspicacious appraisal of the situation *in vivo* (Fig. 7) which has stood the test of time remarkably well. In connection with the increased glycolysis in the hepatoma, and the negligible storage of glycogen, Olson suggested that hexokinase activity and — as was actually demonstrated — 6-phosphofructokinase activity are increased, and argued that "the lower contents of oxidative enzymes and coenzymes in the hepatoma apparently does not compromise the ability of this tissue to carry out the terminal oxidation of carbohydrate at rates comparable to that of the liver cell". Weinhouse[2] came to a similar conclusion, attributing the lactate accumulation to inability of the electron-transport and pyruvate-oxidizing enzymes to cope with the extra load. Supplementation with NAD may be necessary to achieve efficient oxidation of pyruvate.

Catabolism of Carbohydrate via Pyruvate: Newer Observations

Warburg reiterated his views in 1956[5], as did Weinhouse[5] at the other extreme in the acrid controversy concerning tumour respiration and glycolysis. Thus it was shown by Wenner, Spirtes and Weinhouse in 1952[6] that enzymes of the citric acid cycle were not seriously, if at all, depleted in hepatomas compared with liver or in a rhabdosarcoma compared with muscle. The weight of the evidence that has accumulated since 1951 (Potter[8]) rather favours the middle position taken by Olson (see above). At least it seems that a respiratory defect is not a prime cause of cancer.

Observations with isolated mitochondria. Aisenberg[6] showed that the respiratory system of tumour mitochondria operates near its maximum capacity — in contrast with that of mitochondria from normal tissues (none actually homologous with the tumours) — but is quite efficient with respect to rate and to ATP generation. His results seem more convincing than certain evidence adduced[82] for "some defect in an intra-Krebs cycle reaction(s) in tumours".

Mitochondria isolated from hepatomas, or from precancerous liver, are apparently depleted in amount (although not with ethionine feeding, in the author's experience)[41,45,163] and, even with ethionine feeding, are less prone than liver mitochondria to swell *in vitro* (J. C. Arcos[41]); moreover, they are low in NAD and particularly in $NADPH_2$, ATP and other adenosine nucleotides[163]. ("Bound" forms of the nicotinamide-adenine dinucleotides may, however, have been missed in these assays). This depletion of nucleotides was found even in the Morris 5123 hepatoma[163]. The "free" ATPase activity measured in the presence of Mg^{2+} ions is high in supposedly intact mitochondria from precancerous liver or hepatomas, although the rise in hepatomas could be due to necrosis[41] or possibly to the presence of a lipid which damages mitochondria *in vitro* (P. Emmelot, 1961[90]). Such abnormalities in isolated mitochondria could, however, be artefacts due merely to enhanced fragility, in accordance with the degenerative changes seen in hepatomas (although not in precancerous liver) by electron microscopy and with the notably rapid "ageing" *in vitro* as studied particularly by P. Emmelot. This explanation is supported by the finding of Carruthers and Suntzeff[75] that hepatoma mitochondrial fractions are richer in nicotinamide-adenine dinucleotides if prepared with 0·88 M sucrose in place of 0·25 M sucrose — although a raffinose-dextran medium used by Reid[163] gave nucleotide values as low as with 0·25 M sucrose.

Hepatoma mitochondria, if supplemented with NAD, may show normal rates of respiration and ATP generation (Emmelot, 1961[90]; cf. ref. 6), although the pathways for isocitrate oxidation may be somewhat different in nature from those in liver (Hawtrey, 1962[106]). The possibility that tumour cells are inefficient in maintaining the supply of nicotinamide–adenine dinucleotides requisite for active oxidative metabolism will be considered later in this chapter. In general, it would appear that "uncoupling" is prone to occur — perhaps as an *in vitro* artefact — in most hepatomas, the Morris 5123 being an exception (Devlin & Boxer, 1961[45]).

For precancerous liver from ethionine-fed rats, G. L. Fisher reported in 1955[22] that the capacity of mitochondria to oxidize pyruvate was somewhat reduced, perhaps in part due to impaired binding of lipoate (thioctate) by mitochondria; depletion of

CoA[41] might have contributed to the reduction. However, acute treatment with ethionine[22] or dimethylnitrosamine (Emmelot[90]; see also Magee[19]) does not impair mitochondrial respiration or oxidative phosphorylation, nor is there striking impairment with azo-dye feeding. Whilst it seems unlikely that there is a mitochondrial defect crucial to neoplasia, a study of sub-mitochondrial particles might nevertheless prove rewarding.

Integration of metabolic observations. In whole-animal experiments, low recovery of radioactivity in products such as aspartate has been shown for injected pyruvate or acetate by Busch and collaborators[14] with sundry transplanted tumours, and for pyruvate by Muramatsu[142] with primary hepatomas or with late-precancerous liver (the lactate level already being increased in the latter) — although not with only two weeks of azo-dye feeding. Their data do not enable the effect of carcinogenesis on the absolute rate of oxidation to be assessed, but there would appear to be a slowing at least in comparison with the rate of lactate formation. G. L. Fisher reported in 1955[22] that blood pyruvate is elevated in ethionine-fed rats; but unfortunately lactate was not measured.

In studies of individual enzymes concerned in glycolysis, inadequate attention has been paid to enzymes likely to be rate-limiting, and in particular there has been neglect of triose phosphate dehydrogenase, the importance of which has been emphasized by Sir Hans Krebs. Moreover, activities measured with cell-free preparations *in vitro* may be uninformative if no account is taken of the complexities that have become apparent with normal tissues, for example in respect of isoenzymes (e.g. of aldolase — Table 5, Chapter 8), of enzyme conformation as a determinant of activity (Chapter 8), of the balances amongst different processes especially where there is competition for a single substrate, and of the supply of ancillary reactants such as ADP. Recently it has been suggested that phosphofructokinase is normally rate-limiting, in view of its susceptibility to inhibition by ATP (in high concentration) or by citrate (J. V. Passoneau &

O. H. Lowry, 1963). Since, however, there is some evidence (see above) that tumours may be rich in citrate, their high glycolysis cannot be explained on these lines; nor is it likely that the level of inorganic phosphate is so low in tumours as to limit the activity of kinases.

In comparison with normal myeloid leucocytes, leukaemic leucocytes studied *in vitro* have low rates not only of respiration (but see ref. 127) but also of aerobic glycolysis (W. S. Beck[4,6,7,28]; cf. ref. 127). For reasons indicated in Chapter 2, observations on the energy metabolism of ascitic hepatoma cells (Miura[138]) are of doubtful value. While it is an incontrovertible fact that most tumours show changes in energy metabolism (notably acceleration of aerobic glycolysis) that largely accord with Warburg's observations, it can be suggested as a draft epitaph that the changes are really a feature of advanced malignancy. Recent studies *in vitro* with slow-growing transplanted hepatomas, for example in the laboratories of A. C. Aisenberg (see Potter[21]) and of G. Weber[46,201], have shown a good capacity for oxidation of succinate, and a glycolytic rate so low that, as emphasized by Potter[8,21,46], high glycolysis (with a poor Pasteur effect) can hardly be a "minimum deviation". It is nevertheless a deviation possessed by most tumours, and has led to a hypothesis[10] which will be discussed later in this chapter. Moreover, one difficulty in interpretation is that underlying the apparently normal glycolysis observed with hepatomas such as the Morris 5123 there appears to be a possibly crucial fall in hexokinase activity.

Hexokinases and glucose-6-phosphatase. Glucose entry into cells apparently needs the participation of hexokinases, one of which is a specific glucokinase of high K_m. There is little *in vivo* work concerning the efficiency of tumours (compared with homologous normal tissues) in taking up glucose from the blood. Leukaemic leucocytes have a normal or enhanced capacity to convert glucose into glycogen *in vitro*[127], although other work[96] suggests somewhat low activity for hexokinase.

S. Weinhouse and collaborators[46] found that the glucose-phosphorylating capacity of homogenates was hardly changed during azo-dye feeding, but ranged from high in fast-growing hepatomas such as the Novikoff (the K*m* being abnormally low) to low in slow-growing hepatomas such as the Morris 5123. In

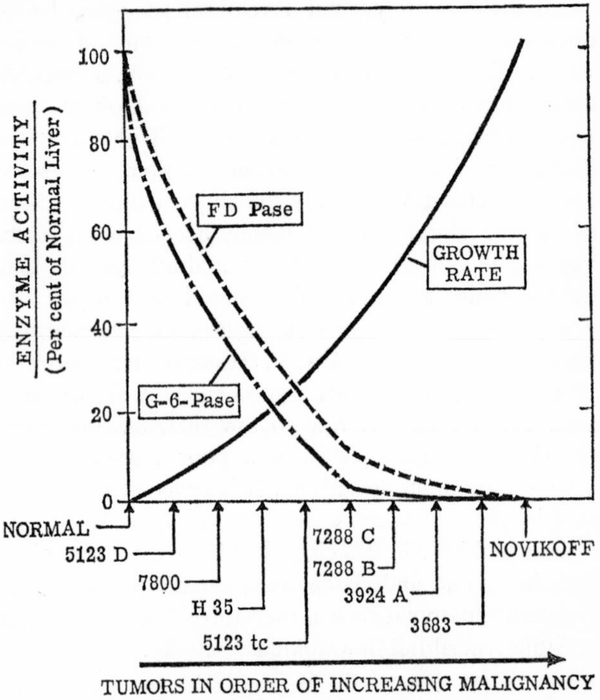

FIG. 8. Correlation of malignancy (tumour growth rate) and glucose-6-phosphatase and fructose-1,6-diphosphatase activities in hepatomas (G. Weber[46]).

another study[191] with a range of tumours, including a hepatoma, high hexokinase activity was found in individual sub-cellular fractions, notably in the mitochondrial fraction, the activity of which is normally low. With slow-growing hepatomas, it was further shown in Weinhouse's laboratory[46] that addition of yeast hexokinase to the homogenates markedly stimulated the phosphorylation of glucose. Assays with slices in G. Weber's laboratory[46,201] showed an almost normal rate of glucose phosphorylation for certain slow-growing hepatomas and, in contrast with the homogenate results, a reduced rate for Novikoff hepatomas. Evidently there is a need for continued investigation of the hexokinase area.

Liver and kidneys are exceptional tissues in having the capacity to liberate glucose into the blood through the action of glucose-6-phosphatase. Glucose-6-phosphatase activity is lacking in many hepatomas, as instanced by the Novikoff hepatoma (G. Weber[45,46]) and a mouse hepatoma[51], but is not drastically depressed in some hepatomas[35] — including some with a fast growth rate[37,163] (Fig. 8). Values for early-precancerous liver, from rats fed azo-dyes or ethionine[22,41], range from normal to half of normal. The presence of glucose-6-phosphatase activity in a particular hepatoma not only reinforces the view that loss of activity is not crucial to neoplasia, but also provides reassurance that the hepatoma arose from parenchymal rather than bile-duct cells (which lack this enzyme).

Glycogen Metabolism and Gluconeogenesis

Hepatomas are usually although not invariably low in glycogen, unlike normal liver from non-fasted rats (*inter alia* refs. 41, 46, 142, 147, 211). A decrease is not consistently found by biochemical analysis after a few weeks of hepatocarcinogen treatment or in acute experiments, and indeed with acetylaminofluorene there may be an increase (Sidransky *et al.*, 1963; see p. 69 in ref. 19). Histochemical analysis may, it is true, disclose local (centrolubular) depletion, undetectable biochemically (J. D. Spain, 1956[41], cf.[102], also K. R. Porter and C. Bruni, 1959[41]). Much of the literature on liver glycogen levels is vitiated by vagueness about the fasting period (if any), but at least it would appear that alterations in glycogen metabolism are unlikely to be requisite for hepatocarcinogenesis.

Glycogen catabolism. With hepatocarcinogenesis there seems to be no consistent change in the capacity for degradation of glycogen to glucose-1-phosphate. Phosphorylase activity, assayed with or without 5′-AMP as a possible activator, was high in Novikoff hepatomas[147] but low in primary hepatomas studied by A. Hadjiolov[9,41] and in liver from ethionine-treated rats studied by K. H. Shull[22,91]. The endogenous level of AMP is not greatly reduced in hepatomas or precancerous liver[163]. Phosphorylase activity in leucocytes is of the normal order in chronic leukaemias[210].

Recent observations by G. Hers (see de Duve[19]) suggest that glycogen catabolism in liver proceeds largely by an amylase pathway. Both this amylase and phosphorylase would presumably have contributed to "amylase" activity as assayed in Greenstein's laboratory[25] — this overall activity being almost normal in a transplanted hepatoma.

Glycogen synthesis. In early studies with hepatomas there was evidence of impaired conversion of pyruvate into carbohydrate (measured as glucose; P. C. Zamecnik[2]); but a benign hepatoma (in CBA mice) studied by Dickens & Weil-Malherbe in 1943[6,*129*] showed little impairment. The conversion can likewise proceed at a good rate with slices from slow-growing hepatomas as studied recently in G. Weber's laboratory[46,201], and almost normal activities have been shown for the individual enzymes concerned — notably fructose-1,6-diphosphatase (Fig. 8) which, like glucose-6-phosphatase, catalyses an irreversible key reaction in gluconeogenesis. The emphasis on fructose-1,6-diphosphatase as a rate-limiting enzyme in gluconeogenesis accords with the views of Sir Hans Krebs; the evidence from his and other laboratories[46] concerning the specificity and control of this enzyme underlines the need for closer study in relation to neoplasia. Certain other enzymes of gluconeogenesis — pyruvate carboxylase and malate dehydrogenase (both concerned in generating oxalacetate), and phophoenolpyruvate carboxykinase (phosphopyruvate carboxylase) — are likewise undiminished in slow-growing hepatomas, although very low in fast-growing hepatomas (G. Weber *et al.*[47,199]).

Glycogen synthesis from glucose needs the participation of phosphoglucomutase, the level of which was shown in G. Weber's laboratory to be somewhat low even in certain slow-growing hepatomas[46,201]. Some such hepatomas, however, have proved to surpass normal liver with respect to the ability of slices to convert glucose into glycogen. An enhanced capacity to convert glucose into glycogen has also been found with leucocytes in conditions such as acute leukaemia and chronic myelosis[127]. Taking account of results for hexokinase (see above) and of the following data, it can at least be concluded that glycogen synthesis is not necessarily blocked in neoplasia.

The final steps in glycogen synthesis, whether from glucose or from pyruvate, proceed through UDPglucose. The pyrophosphorylase through which glucose-1-phosphate is converted into UDPglucose has normal activity in the Morris 5123 hepatoma[163], is somewhat low in primary hepatomas[163], and is low but nevertheless still present in the Novikoff hepatoma[147]. No hepatoma so far studied has shown a serious lack of UDPglucose itself[163], nor of the transferase whereby UDPglucose is converted into glycogen[163]. The latter enzyme, however, does warrant further investigation in the light of the complexities recently shown with normal tissues.

Pentose-phosphate Cycle

Carbohydrate catabolism in normal tissues proceeds mainly by the classical pathways discussed above; but usually, besides a minor contribution from the UDPglucose-UDPglucuronate-ascorbate pathway (probably limited by UDPglucuronate formation, which is little affected by hepatocarcinogenesis[163]), there is some contribution from the pentose-phosphate cycle (hexose-monophosphate shunt). Late steps in this complex cycle have been little studied in relation to neoplasia, but much attention has been given to the first step — NADP-dependent conversion of glucose-

6-phosphate into 6-phosphogluconate — which does in fact appear to be the rate-limiting step.

Glucose-6-phosphate dehydrogenase. Transplanted tumours in general, as compared with a range of normal tissues, show glucose-6-phosphate dehydrogenase activity of the normal order, although sarcomas tend to be higher than lymphomas (G. E. Glock and P. McLean, 1954[129]). High activity has been found in a rhabdosarcoma compared with muscle[139], and in various hepatomas compared with normal or regenerating liver[41,163,200] — although almost normal activity has been found in the Morris 5123 hepatoma[201]. High activity has also been found in liver from rats fed azo-dyes[129,163] and, contrary to observations from Emmelot's laboratory[41], in hyperplastic nodules which may be benign forerunners of hepatocarcinomas. (Feeding conditions might well influence the outcome of tissue comparisons with respect to this enzyme activity, which is normally very variable as pointed out by Potter[21]). Studies with leucocytes by W. S. Beck, J. R. Bertino, and their respective collaborators[3] (see also M. Cortoli *et al.*[4]) have shown reduced activity in leukaemia, chronic (myeloid or lymphatic) or acute.

Evidently, then, a rise in glucose-6-phosphate dehydrogenase activity is not an essential step in neoplasia, although it may well be important as a late step. In certain experimental situations as studied in the Teppermans' laboratory[46], increases in glucose-6-phosphate dehydrogenase activity appear to be secondary to increases in the rate of lipogenesis; but in neoplasia the rate of lipogenesis is not usually increased (see below). The literature on 6-phosphogluconate dehydrogenase, concerned in the second step of the pentose phosphate cycle, does not point to a rate-limiting function either in normal or in neoplastic tissue.

Overall rate of the cycle. Increased activity of glucose-6-phosphate dehydrogenase as measured *in vitro*, with excess NADP present, does not itself prove that there is faster operation of the cycle *in vivo*, particularly since the level of NADP is usually depleted in tumours (see below). For assessment of the contribution of the cycle to glucose catabolism in whole-cell preparations, the use of glucose isotopically labelled in different positions can give useful information if judiciously interpreted. This approach, as applied to slices in the laboratories of I. L. Chaikoff, S. Kit and G. Weber[6,30,46], has pointed to acceleration of the cycle in a range of hepatomas and in lymphosarcomas (compared with normal lymphatic tissues), but not in a mammary carcinoma compared with lactating mammary gland (the latter itself having high activity) or in a primary liver tumour studied by B. W. Agranoff and collaborators[6]. Similar experiments with homogenates have suggested faster operation of the cycle in azo-dye hepatomas, although not early in the dye feeding[119]. The isotopic results are, then, broadly in accord with the enzymic data.

For a summary of the relationship of changes in the pentose-phosphate cycle, and of other parameters of energy metabolism, to hepatoma growth rate, reference may be made to Chapter 8, Table 4.

Levels and Metabolism of Nicotinamide-adenine Dinucleotides

Much published work on the levels of these "pyridine" nucelotides is of limited value, because of failure to determine each nucleotide individually or to compare tumours with homologous normal tissues, or because the actual procedures for extraction and estimation were at fault. Too much weight has sometimes been placed[9] on the tendency for NAD to fall with neoplasia.

Tissue levels. There are reports of a fall in liver NAD after brief treatment with hepatotoxic agents such as ethionine[187] or after several weeks of treatment with various hepatocarcinogens[157]. However, a marked fall in NAD is not consistently found in precancerous liver or hepatomas — either in whole tissue or in mitochondrial fractions — according to the data of Glock and McLean (1957[41]), of Nodes and Reid[163], and of other workers (see Le Breton & Moulé[12]). The scanty information for non-hepatic tumours as compared with homologous normal tissues is considered below.

For $NADH_2$ and also for $NADPH_2$, there is indeed evidence of serious depletion in hepatomas, and of some depletion in precancerous liver (for citations see Aisenberg[6], Le Breton & Moulé[12], Nodes & Reid[163], Weber[200]); thus with ethionine feeding the decrease in $NADH_2$ is proportionately greater than that in NAD[187]. Observations reported by B. Chance[46], that liver (unlike kidney) shows a fall in the ratio $NADH_2$/NAD with anoxia, suggest that the fall in hepatomas might be a symptom of anoxia due to poor vascularity. At present the data warrant only the generalization that hepatomas are apparently low in the *reduced* forms of NAD and of NADP; one reason for caution is the observation of Jedeikin and Weinhouse (see Le Breton & Moulé[12]) that a rhabdosarcoma had a level of $NADH_2$ similar to that in muscle, although a low level of NAD. Lymphosarcomas studied by Glock and McLean[41] had levels of NAD and $NADH_2$ similar to those in thymus. Leucocytes have shown a rise in NAD in chronic myeloid leukaemia and especially in acute leukaemia, with normal levels of $NADH_2$, NADP and $NADPH_2$[183]. Usually, however, the levels of NADP and especially of $NADPH_2$ are diminished with neoplasia; the fall in NADP may be greater than would appear from conventional assays, since hepatomas seem to lack the "acid-labile NADP" recently demonstrated with normal liver in O. H. Lowry's laboratory[78]. The evidence for a "reductive environment" in tumour cells (Novikoff[7]) seems to be weak.

Rates of biosynthesis and catabolism. Reports from the laboratories of J. H. Quastel and of P. Emmelot[6,41] suggest that the capacity for NAD breakdown ("DPNase") is high in primary hepatomas but not in all tumours. R. K. Morton expressed the view in 1958[41,45] that a low level of NAD, as is indeed found in some tumours, is attributable not to faster breakdown but to slower synthesis from nicotinamide mononucleotide through the action of NAD pyrophosphorylase. This pyrophosphorylase, which is unusual in being confined to the nucleus, was reduced to one-fifth of normal in a mammary carcinoma compared with lactating mammary gland, and in a mouse hepatoma compared with liver — as later confirmed for the Novikoff hepatoma (there being no evidence of an inhibitor)[195], although "minimum-deviation" hepatomas have yet to be investigated. In these studies the values were calculated per nucleus, and the decreases might have been less if calculated per gram (cf. Chapter 2, Baselines for Expressing Results); altogether it is by no means established that NAD synthesis is commonly a bottleneck in tumours. At least there are no early effects of hepatocarcinogens such as dimethylnitrosamine on the activity of the enzyme (although this may be low in regenerating liver)[188]. Recently it has been shown that the precursor of NAD is the mononucleotide of nicotinate rather than of nicotinamide, but there is no indication of the existence of a different pyrophosphorylase such that the above observations would become invalid[188].

In other studies the capacity for NAD synthesis has been tested *in vivo* by measuring the rise in liver NAD after injection of nicotinamide. Impaired synthesis has been found with an ascitic hepatoma[33], and with liver from rats given an azo-dye[119] or ethionine[188]; with the latter agent at least, there was no indication of faster breakdown of NAD. M. Revel and P. Mandel[33] have put forward (in 1962) an ingenious but perhaps over-extended hypothesis akin to those put forward in 1958 by Morton[41] and by Sahasrabudhe[173], that underlying acceleration of cell growth there is a fall in NAD synthesis and diversion of ATP into nucleic-acid synthesis.

The kinase which catalyses the synthesis of NADP from NAD shows unchanged activity in early-precancerous liver (although a fall in NADP level is already evident) and a moderate fall in primary hepatomas[78]. The tendency for NADP to fall more than NAD might be due rather to faster catabolism of NADP, as found (together with faster catabolism of NAD) in Emmelot's laboratory with mitochondrial fractions from hepatomas.

Re-oxidation of the reduced nucleotides. $NADH_2$ is constantly being formed through cellular oxidations, as is $NADPH_2$ especially in connection with the oxidation of fat and of glucose-6-phosphate (by the pentose-phosphate cycle). Transhydrogenase, the activity of which is low in certain hepatomas (B. Reynafarje & V. R. Potter, 1957[45]) but high in leukaemic leucocytes[183], normally provides a link whereby any inadequacy in the rate of re-oxidation of $NADPH_2$ could be overcome by reaction with NAD to yield $NADH_2$ and NADP. However, little is known about the importance of this link in normal tissues; in any case the link would be useless unless there were efficient oxidation of $NADH_2$ to NAD.

In assays of sub-cellular fractions from liver for $NADH_2$-cytochrome *c* reductase, activity is usually found partly in mitochondrial fractions but mainly in microsomal fractions (although the converse was found by Reynafarje & Potter[45]). The physiological role of the microsomal activity is obscure, since cytochrome *c* and cytochrome oxidase are both lacking in microsomes, although certain other cytochromes are present[145]. The mitochondrial activity, at least in muscle, may be due to as many as three different systems, each involving flavoprotein; one system does not need the participation of any cytochrome other than cytochrome *c*. It seems unlikely that $NADH_2$-cytochrome *c* reductase activity is normally a limiting factor in *intra*-mitochondrial oxidations. Some oxidation of $NADPH_2$ can occur through a microsomal oxidase (with no addition of cytochrome *c*), accompanied by peroxidation of microsomal lipids, the significance of which is not yet clear (P. Hochstein and L. Ernster[19]).

Some activity of $NADPH_2$-cytochrome *c* reductase is present in microsomes, but most is found in mitochondrial fractions and may be due to systems analogous to two of the mitochondrial $NADH_2$-cytochrome *c* reductase systems mentioned above.

Subtle study of these complex systems has yet to be made on tumours, and indeed the normal role of the microsomes in energy metabolism is not clear. At least it appears that the overall activity of $NADH_2$-cytochrome *c* reductase in homogenates or mitochondrial fractions is not drastically reduced in Novikoff hepatomas and is almost normal in certain other hepatomas and in precancerous liver[41,45]. Data for $NADPH_2$-cytochrome *c* reductase suggest a drastic fall[41,45] (not confirmed by Novikoff[7]). "Minimum-deviation hepatomas" have been little studied.

"Shuttle" system for $NADH_2$ re-oxidation. Since $NADH_2$ generated *outside* the mitochondria apparently cannot be efficiently re-oxidized *in situ*, it is presumably re-oxidized by some route which leads to the terminal electron-transport system of the mitochondria, and which circumvents the apparent impermeability of the mitochondrial membrane to $NADH_2$. It appears in fact that there are two such routes. One involves the α-glycerophosphate dehydrogenase of mitochondria — an enzyme which, at least relative to lactate dehydrogenase, is low in tumours (see Potter[46]) as shown in the laboratories of G. E. Boxer, Th. Bücher, P. Emmelot (but see ref. 90), H. Holzer, P. U. Angeletti (who compared a rhabdosarcoma with muscle), and M. Cortoli[4] (who studied animal leukaemias). This generalization holds also for many slow-growing hepatomas, even if regenerating rather than normal liver is taken as the reference tissue.

These observations were claimed to offer an explanation of the high glycolysis usually found in tumours[10]. Because of the lowered ratio of α-glycerophosphate dehydrogenase to lactate dehydrogenase, $NADH_2$ formed by oxidation of glyceraldehyde-3-phosphate would be re-oxidized mainly by reaction with pyruvate (giving lactate), rather than through the "α-glycerophosphate shuttle" which seems to be a device for overcoming the impermeability of the mitochondrial membrane to $NADH_2$ (Fig. 9). The Morris 5123 hepatoma is exceptional in not having a low ratio of the two dehydrogenases, but it appears to have a defect in an alternative device — the "acetoacetate shuttle" (Fig. 9)[10]. The theory centered on α-glycerophosphate has in fact been adversely criticized[90] although by no means demolished.

The various observations concerning the re-oxidation of $NADH_2$ and $NADPH_2$ hardly throw light on the tendency for the ratios $NADH_2/NAD$ and $NADPH_2/NADP$ to be low in hepatomas compared with liver (normal or regenerating). The disproportionately low level of $NADPH_2$ cannot moreover, be due to inefficient reduction of NADP by the pentose–phosphate cycle (see above), nor to depressed oxidation of fatty acids in view of data now to be discussed.

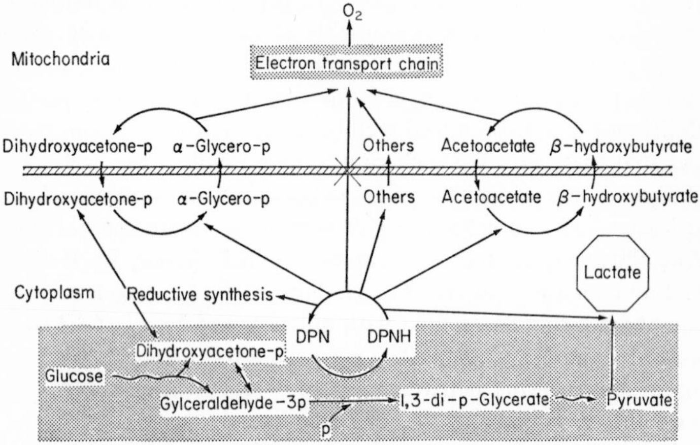

FIG. 9. Pathways of intracellular hydrogen transport, with particular reference to the re-oxidation of DPNH ($NADH_2$) generated by glycolysis in the cell sap (G. E. Boxer & T. M. Devlin[10]; copyright 1961 by the American Association for the Advancement of Science). The hatched line denotes the mitochondrial membrane, and the cross at the intersection of this line with the vertical arrow denotes the "lack of direct reaction of DPNH with the mitochondrial oxidation system in either normal or malignant tissues"[10].

Fatty Acid Metabolism

Tumours are sometimes low in lipids (Chapter 4), but no conclusion can be drawn from this observation alone, particularly since accumulation rather than loss of neutral fat is often seen in precancerous liver[45]. Such accumulation, as found with many hepatotoxic agents, might be due to impaired production of the particular proteins required for the transport of lipid to the cell exterior (E. Farber[22], K. R. Rees[19]).

Catabolism. Assays with tributyrin as substrate have shown a reduced rate of hydrolysis by cell-free preparations from hepatomas, although for some hepatomas the reduction was small[41]. Hepatoma slices incubated with labelled palmitate (Weinhouse[2]) or octanoate (Chaikoff[6,51]) have shown an almost normal rate of oxidation. With acetate, for which a different activating enzyme is required, poor oxidation was found by Chaikoff's group[6] but not by Olson[2]. Isolated mitochondria have shown almost normal rates of oxidation of hexanoate or palmitate in the case of certain hepatomas studied in Emmelot's laboratory[32,41], and of octanoate in the case of precancerous liver[6,41,45]; with the hepatomas it was particularly important to supplement the system with NAD because of loss from the mitochondria. (Supplementation with NADP seems not to have been tried.) Poor oxidation of fatty acids as found in early studies with hepatoma homogenates (C. G. Baker & A. Meister, 1950[6]) might have been due to insufficiency of NAD(P).

In Emmelot's laboratory, adenomatous primary hepatomas (as distinct from the trabecular type; see Histology, Chapter 1) showed poor oxidation of fatty acids by mitochondrial fractions even if NAD were added. From the scanty data available (see also E. A. Neifakh[32]) it would appear that inefficiency in this respect is not a universal property of hepatomas studied *in vitro*; but the possibility remains that the supply of a factor such as CoA might be inadequate *in vivo*. The oxidation of acetate, and its conversion into acetoacetate (which was slow with hepatoma slices studied in Weinhouse's laboratory[41,45]), are particularly in need of closer investigation.

Biosynthesis. It now appears that there are two possible pathways for the synthesis of fatty acids, both requiring CoA and $NADPH_2$. One is the mitochondrial ("elongation") system, and the other the extra-mitochondrial ("malonyl-CoA") system.

There is no information on the behaviour of either system in cell-free preparations from tumours as compared with homologus normal tissues.

With slices, Olsen[2] found that the conversion of acetate into fatty acids and also into cholesterol proceeded almost as rapidly with a primary hepatoma as with liver (cf. Fig. 7). Accelerated conversion of glucose into fatty acids was seen with a mouse hepatoma in Chaikoff's laboratory[6,51], but Novikoff or Morris 5123 hepatomas have shown the converse (with glucose or pyruvate)[45]. Weinhouse and co-workers[41] found markedly impaired conversion of acetate into fatty acids as well as aceto-acetate (but not into cholesterol or CO_2) with slices from primary hepatomas, although not with slices from precancerous liver. Such impairment might be a reflection of insufficiency of CoA, or possibly of $NADPH_2$, although in Chaikoff's view, the level of $NADPH_2$ is in general not an actual determinant of the rate of fatty-acid synthesis.

Whilst it seems unlikely that a defect in the synthesis or catabolism of fatty acids (as distinct from phospholipids) will prove to be an essential step in the neoplastic transformation, there is evidently a need for closer investigation in the light of present-day knowledge.

CHAPTER 6

Protein Metabolism

IN the following survey of the wide field of protein and amino-acid metabolism, the emphasis is again on differences between tumours and homologous normal tissues (on a wet-weight basis). Among the diverse changes reported for cancerous or pecancerous tissues, a few perhaps warrant closer study (particularly in "minimum-deviation" hepatomas) as possible pointers to the nature of the neoplastic transformation. Certain of the changes to be mentioned may at least rank as attributes of advanced malignancy.

Protein and Amino-acid Levels

Several early studies of tumour "amino acids" refer not to free amino acids but to amino acids derived by hydrolysis of the proteins, and can be written off as uninformative. There is, however, a case for investigation of a recent claim[173] that aspartate is lacking (perhaps replaced by valine) in the DNA-linked proteins of azo-dye hepatomas, perhaps because of diversion of aspartate into carbamoylaspartate synthesis (cf. below, Urea synthesis).

Free amino acids. In a series of transplanted hepatomas, G. Weber and co-workers[47a] found no consistent abnormality in the overall level of amino-acids. From semi-quantitative analyses for individual amino acids, S. Roberts[17,28] concluded that different tumours resembled one another (in accordance with the "convergence hypothesis" of Greenstein[25]) and that there were no consistent differences between tumours and homologous normal tissues. The results do suggest that glutamate may be high in tumours compared with corresponding normal tissues, and that glutamine may be low at least in hepatomas; but Muramatsu[142] noted a fall in glutamate (and also in alanine and aspartate) in primary hepatomas and in precancerous liver. For glutamine, however, there is a supporting observation from analyses on transplanted lymphosarcomas (S. Kit[30]). These, in comparison with lymphatic tissues, were low in glutamine, aspartate and ethanolamine phosphate but high in proline (as for the Morris 5123 hepatoma[152]) and in threonine, alanine and glycine; moreover, in disagreement with Greenstein's hypothesis, the pattern in the lymphosarcomas differed from that in a "carcinosarcoma". For histidine there is a report (S. Perugini[4]) of a high content in leukaemic cells.

Amino-acid levels are, of course, merely a reflection of metabolic balances, and changes in level are difficult to interpret. At least there is a case for further measurements of glutamine, in view of its special metabolic importance as will be mentioned later.

Proteins in sub-cellular fractions. Analyses on unfractionated tumours show no drastic depletion in protein content, but analyses on sub-cellular fractions have shown, for the protein of mitochondrial and microsomal fractions, a reduced content in hepatomas with the possible exception of primary hepatomas produced by acetylaminofluorene[14,37,41,163]. Mitochondrial and microsomal fractions also show a decrease in yield when hepatocarcinogens are fed[163], although (in the author's experience) ethionine is a striking exception which vitiates an otherwise good correlation with carcinogenicity. (Mitochondrial-fraction protein is, moreover, depressed by α-naphthylisothiocyanate, which is non-carcinogenic). For tumours other than hepatomas, data as obtained by A. Laird[30] lack a normal-tissue base-line.

There have been few studies with purified nuclei as distinct from crude "nuclear" fractions. The average ratio of protein to DNA was normal in nuclei from primary hepatomas studied by Moulé and Chauveau[12,41], but was high in a mouse hepatoma because of a rise in "residual protein"[174].

Protein patterns. Early studies on individual soluble proteins from mitochondrial fractions showed loss of at least one ultracentrifugal component in a mouse hepatoma (G. Hogeboom & W. C. Schneider[30]), and alterations in electrophoretic pattern in liver from rats fed an azo dye (G. de Lamirande and collaborators). In the latter study, loss of a component from supernatant fractions was also observed. S. Sorof[41] thoroughly examined supernatant fractions by ultracentrifugation and especially by electrophoresis (also, more recently, by gel filtration[186]; see also B. W. Moore *et al.*[32]). One particularly striking result was that "slow h_2 proteins", which are basic and have a high capacity for binding azo dyes, were high in precancerous liver (the correlation with the carcinogenicity of the agents being good) but were absent from hepatomas. Although it is disconcerting that Morris 5123 hepatomas and ethionine-induced hepatomas do contain "slow h_2 proteins" (see Potter[8]; Sorof[16a]), nuclei from the hepatomas await checking for a deficiency as in azo-dye hepatoma nuclei[16a].

The study of microsomal proteins has been rather unrewarding, but there is indirect evidence that the level of a particular haemprotein may be low in the Morris 5123 hepatoma[145]; moreover, azo-dye hepatomas are low in certain basic proteins, at least one of which may be microsomal[114].

Certain rhabdosarcomas ("adult-type") studied immunologically have shown loss of myosin (D. Pressman[1]). The chromatographic pattern of proteins extracted from a rhabdosarcoma had previously been found to differ from that of muscle, for example in having a lower proportion of basic components (myogen and myoglobin?) as if there were loss of specialization[139]. The pattern for the rhabdosarcoma resembled that previously found[139] for a squamous-cell carcinoma of mouse skin. The pattern for the latter carcinoma was grossly similar to that for normal epidermis[139]; but a basal cell tumour (human) differed from epidermis — notably in lacking a specific keratin fraction[170]. It is in fact unusual for protein patterns to be strikingly abnormal with cancer, as in the special case of plasmocytoma (multiple myeloma) where the neoplastic plasmocytes produce "Bence-Jones" and other abnormal proteins[14].

The scanty information so far obtained by immunochemical procedures hardly justifies speculations such as those of H. N. Green[48] on lipoprotein antigens. Alterations in antigen pattern, with appearance of an extra antigen which contained bound carcinogen, were found by R. Baldwin[31] in precancerous liver, in accordance with findings by T. A. Korosteleva and other Russian workers. Both in liver and skin, carcinogenesis leads to the appearance of a "tumour-specific antigen", located in the microsomal fraction (but conceivably derived from the plasma membrane) and possibly different for different tumours. On the other hand, most workers emphasize loss of antigens (C. Deckers[32], P. Emmelot[13a], J. H. F. Maisin[32,132]), as in the rhabdosarcoma mentioned above. With hepatocarcinogenesis at least one of the antigens revealed by the use of fluorescent antibodies disappears from parenchymal cells (E. Weiler[48]; cf. ref. 99), and there may be "auto-immunity" as shown by the appearance of antibodies in the blood[69]. Pressman[1] has observed, in line with observations by R. C. Nairn (see H. Friedrich-Frekesa *et al.*[21]), that primary-hepatoma cells are often not stainable by antibodies (fluorescent) to normal-liver microsomal proteins. Generalization about hepatomas would be dangerous because of evidence for individual variations in antigen pattern.

Protein patterns in relation to enzymic activity. The study of protein components will gain in value when, with enzymic assays on well resolved peaks, the components can be functionally characterized. The technique of starch-gel electrophoresis has already shown promise in this connection. Following early electrophoretic studies by G. L. Miller and collaborators, P. U. Angeletti and co-workers[139] studied the location of certain enzymes in chromatograms (DEAE-SF resin) and noted differences in the number and distribution of enzyme-activity peaks in certain tumours compared with homologous normal tissues. In general the tumours showed no deletions: in fact, for glucose-6-phosphate dehydrogenase an epidermal carcinoma had three peaks instead of two, and a rhabdosarcoma had three peaks instead of one. Such studies are, of course, informative in connection with the iso-enzyme problem (Chapter 8), particularly if individual peaks are characterized in respects such as substrate specificity and susceptibility to allosteric control.

Sulphydryl Compounds

The important topic of —SH compounds is best considered in connection with proteins and amino acids, although measurements of —SH groups have seldom included delineation of the compounds concerned. Reduced glutathione is particularly important amongst acid-soluble —SH compounds, but according to Calcutt[72] it represents barely one-third of the "acid-soluble —SH". A common and serious fault in the untidy literature is imprecision in stating whether —SH measurements refer to total —SH, protein —SH (after denaturation?), or non-protein —SH. Not only are there differences in methodology among laboratories, but conclusions have sometimes been drawn from a few scattered results, with little regard to diurnal variations as recently shown for normal liver[71].

There is an early report[41] of a normal level of non-protein —SH in azo-dye hepatomas; but other literature cited by Calcutt in 1961[72] suggests that hepatomas are low in —SH. V. B. Mitbander and collaborators[*161*] recently stated that azo-dye feeding leads to a fall in "total" —SH or, as stated in a graph legend, "free" —SH. However, other literature for precancerous liver suggests an increase in —SH, protein or non-protein[41]; in acute experiments at least, reduced glutathione in particular is increased[146] as first shown by Boyland & Mawson in 1938[*146*].

From literature surveyed in 1961, Calcutt[72] concluded that an increase in "target-tissue' —SH is a general phenomenon during chemical carcinogenesis. For example, in his laboratory a rise in "total" —SH was seen in liver from ethionine-fed rats, in the lungs of mice given urethane, and in skin treated with 3,4-benzpyrene or with a co-carcinogen (croton oil). The rise was considered to be a feature of the "co-carcinogenic or tumour development phase", the level being low rather than high in tumours and also in skin *briefly* treated with a carcinogen such as benzpyrene. The changes in precancerous tissues or tumours may be more consistent for non-protein —SH than for protein —SH, as in the case of a lymphoma (which tended to have lower acid-soluble —SH than thymus)[71].

Two recent reports have cast doubt on the supposition that a rise in —SH consistently occurs during carcinogenesis. During tumour induction by dimethylbenzanthracene in the hamster cheek pouch[140], increased —SH (acid-soluble) was found only in males and then only at 36 hours; in general the precancerous tissue showed a decrease, as did the carcinomas. No change was found in the total —SH of mouse epidermis during carcinogenesis by methylcholanthrene[125].

In chronic granulocytic leukaemia, a fall in the free —SH of leucocytes (apparently reduced glutathione) is largely offset by a rise in —S—S—, there being no —S—S— in normal leucocytes[104]. Otherwise there seems to be little information on —S—S— levels. (See below for observations on cystine catabolism.)

It is uncertain what causes a change in —SH level, or what is the metabolic implication of such a change. The rise found in pre-cancerous liver by some authors accords with the finding of a moderate rise in the activity of glutathione reductase (E. G. Trams[41]). A change in —SH level might have implications for cell division, in advance of which the nucleus shows —SH stainability and a rise occurs in the —SH (with a fall in —S—S—) of a protein fraction soluble in 25 per cent trichloracetic acid and possibly located in the cytoplasm (L. Rapkine, D. Mazia, K. Dan). Evidently there is a need for continued work on —SH and —S—S— levels, with attention to individual compounds and to individual sub-cellular fractions.

Catabolism

Consideration will be given first to protein itself, then to amino acids. The conclusions rest mainly on assays of cell-free preparations for enzymic activity.

Protein catabolism. Those cathepsins (intracellular proteinases) which act at a pH more alkaline than 5·0, as studied in the laboratories of J. P. Greenstein[25], P. C. Zamecnik[211] and Y. Miura[138], have shown increased or else unchanged activity in hepatomas, but have not received the attention they deserve. Cathepsin activity, being higher at acid pH values, has more commonly been assayed at pH 3·5–5·0, with diverse substrates. Under conditions which would liberate activity from lysosomes — the extent of such liberation being uncertain in some reports — the activity at acid pH is increased in precancerous liver, but shows variable changes (sometimes a decrease) in hepatomas, depending on the hepatoma and on the substrate[41,138,211]. Under conditions of homogenization which would keep the lysosomal activity latent, the "free" activity (as found in supernatant fractions) shows an increase relative to total activity in Novikoff hepatomas (C. Allard *et al.*, 1957[41]; assays at pH 3·6) and an absolute increase in primary hepatomas[41]. Cathepsin activity at pH 3·5, and also dipeptidase activity, have been reported to rise in precancerous epidermis but not in the papillomas and tumours eventually obtained[125].

Judging particularly from the results for "free" activity — which conceivably comes from digestive or autophagic vacuoles that rupture during homogenizing (de Duve[19]; see Chapter 1, Electron Microscopy) — there may be accelerated breakdown of at least certain proteins in the precancerous or cancerous cell.

Amino-acid catabolism. The only generalization that can be made about amino-acid catabolism is that it is not consistently suppressed. For one amino acid — histidine — evidence has been obtained for accelerated decarboxylation (with an increase in urinary histamine), both in liver after administration of dimethyl-nitrosamine[164] and in a transplanted hepatoma when it had grown large[115]. For the main route of amino-acid catabolism — oxidative deamination — there are only scattered observations.

Experiments with perfused liver by W. T. Burke and L. L. Miller[41,45] showed a depression during azo-dye feeding in the overall catabolism of various amino acids to urea (the formation of which is discussed below) and to CO_2; the depression in histidine catabolism accorded with earlier observations for hepatomas[45]. V. H. Auerbach & H. A. Waisman reported in 1958[45] that the Novikoff hepatoma — compared with host liver — lacked enzymes such as threonine and serine dehydrases and tryptophan pyrrolase (peroxidase). The latter enzyme is also low in primary hepatomas induced by azo dyes or ethionine[37,41] but not in certain transplanted hepatomas of slow growth rate[88] (cf. Chapter 8, Fig. 13; and Pitot[37,46], Potter[8,46]). In rats fed azo dyes for several weeks, Kizer and collaborators[41] found a fall in serine dehydrase, but the fall was unrelated to carcinogenicity. Moreover, almost normal activities of threonine and serine dehydrases have been found in certain slow-growing hepatomas (Potter[8,46], Pitot[37,46]), although the rate of proline oxidation did appear to be low[152].

Tissue-slice experiments with various hepatomas and with regenerating liver have shown normal rates of oxidation for serine, and also for alanine, aspartate and glycine; for isoleucine and valine the rate actually tended to be high in fast-growing hepatomas, but for no amino acid was there an exact correlation with growth rate[199].

The level of glutamate dehydrogenase, to which particular attention has been devoted in the laboratories of P. Emmelot, G. de Lamirande and H. C. Pitot, is normal in precancerous liver and seems low in many hepatomas[9,41,45] — perhaps as an artefact (Novikoff[7]). In certain slow-growing hepatomas, and even in some primary hepatomas, the level is almost normal[37]. During epidermal carcinogenesis a fall in activity was seen as early as one day after the application of methylcholanthrene, no hyperplasia being evident at that time[125].

The supposed fall in "cystine desulphurase" (really cystine reductase+cysteine desulphurase) in tumours seems to be a reflection of deficiency of pyridoxal phosphate and of NADH[9,2].

The significance of the reported fall in D-amino-acid oxidase in precancerous liver[41] is uncertain, since early reports of a high content of D-amino acids in tumour proteins have not been confirmed.

Urea synthesis. In the disposal of the ammonia liberated by oxidative deamination of amino acids, its conversion into urea normally proceeds via citrulline and arginine. According to F. Cedrangolo and collaborators[129] there may be an alternative pathway to urea — a possibility recognized by Burke & Miller[41] — but its importance is not yet known.

In primary hepatomas, there is a drastic fall in carbamoylphosphate synthetase and in each of the four enzymes concerned in the synthesis of urea from carbamoylphosphate and ammonia[129], viz:

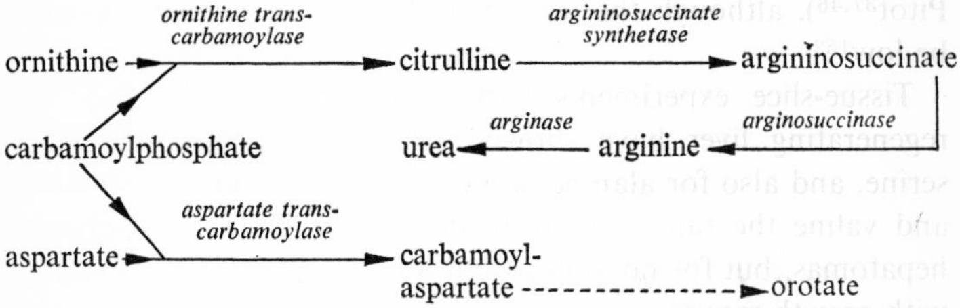

Carbamoylphosphate synthetase and ornithine transcarbamoylase were only moderately reduced in certain slow-growing hepatomas as studied by Potter[8] and by other workers[129], There has been no study of slow-growing hepatomas with respect to the next three enzymes, the first of which (argininosuccinate synthetase, "condensing enzyme") seems to be the rate-limiting enzyme in arginine formation. Azo-dye feeding for several weeks leads — provided that the dyes are carcinogenic — to a striking decrease in carbamoylphosphate synthetase (following an initial increase) and also in ornithine transcarbamoylase; but only the latter is decreased with ethionine feeding[129].

Although loss of ornithine transcarbamoylase can hardly be an essential step in the neoplastic transformation, it may be an important characteristic of fast-growing hepatomas. There is a tendency for aspartate transcarbamoylase to show a rise in absolute activity (Chapter 7) or at least in activity relative to that of ornithine transcarbamoylase; thereby the diminished supply of carbamoylphosphate could be conserved for synthesis of carbamoylaspartate rather than of urea (Potter, McLean *et al.*[129]).

The last step in urea synthesis, mediated by arginase and probably not rate-limiting, has been extensively studied in tumours. Various studies on hepatomas have shown low activities[41]; but in an epidermal carcinoma as compared with normal or hyperplastic (precancerous) epidermis there was a ten-fold rise in activity, although the tissue level of urea remained low[17]. The arginase activity of leucocytes is of the normal order in chronic as distinct from acute leukaemia (myeloid or lymphatic)[58]. Precancerous liver does not consistently show a striking decrease in arginase[129]. Further study of this enzyme is hardly likely to throw light on how neoplasia is produced.

The conclusion from the enzymic measurements outlined above, that the induction of fast-growing hepatomas entails impaired urea synthesis, accords with tissue-slice findings obtained as early as 1943 by Dickens & Weil-Malherbe[6,*129*], who further observed that there was little impairment in slices from benign hepatomas arising spontaneously in CBA mice. The conclusion also accords with results obtained in liver-perfusion experiments already mentioned (Burke & Miller[41,45]): there was reduced formation of urea from ornithine in precancerous liver, but, paradoxically, urea formation from ammonia or glutamine was not reduced, perhaps because of operation of an alternative pathway for urea synthesis. Other observations concerning glutamine will be mentioned in a later paragraph.

Amino-acid Supply

In connection with the question of amino-acid supply, mention should be made of the concept (G. B. Mider[25]) that a tumour acts as a "nitrogen trap" by virtue of a high avidity for blood-borne amino acids. Such avidity, although corroborated by recent Russian work[153] and exalted into a general theory of cancer by G. Wiseman and P. N. Ghadialli, has been questioned by G. Rouser and collaborators[28] (cf. ref. 104) on the basis of results with leucocytes — although A. S. Weisberger and B. Levine[9] had previously found a high uptake of glycine and cyst(e)ine by leukaemic leucocytes.

Among special reactions concerned with the synthesis of particular amino acids, the synthesis of proline from pyrroline-5-carboxylate warrants attention in view of the high enzymic activity found in a slow-growing hepatoma[152]. Neoplasia could conceivably entail accelerated synthesis of methionine, histidine and serine, since — at least in leukaemic leucocytes — the supply of folate seems to be increased[36] and, moreover, with chronic lymphoid leukaemia there is a rise in serine hydroxymethylase (serine aldolase; J. R. Bertino and collaborators[3]).

The biosynthesis of "non-essential" amino acids is essentially a facet of carbohydrate catabolism. There is no reason to believe that tumours are seriously deficient in the requisite α-oxo acids (Chapter 5). Consideration will now be given to transamination processes, with no implication that these should be regarded as anabolic rather than catabolic.

Transaminases. As first postulated by P. P. Cohen in 1942, there may be an inverse correlation between the activity of transaminase (particularly glutamate-oxalacetate) and the rate of tissue growth in diverse experimental situations. The rationale for such a correlation is not obvious; enzymes which serve to maintain a balance amongst certain amino acids would hardly be expected to govern cell growth, and if tumours indeed act as a "nitrogen trap" there should be no bottle-neck in amino-acid supply.

Decreased activity of transaminases (glutamate-oxalacetate or -pyruvate) is indeed found in primary hepatomas[41], although both increases and decreases have been reported for precancerous liver[41]. The Novikoff hepatoma is very low in glutamate-oxalacetate transaminase and also, according to Auerbach & Waisman[45, 129], in tyrosine-oxoglutarate transaminase. The latter enzyme is normal in one slow-growing hepatoma (Morris 7316) at least compared with host liver (Pitot[46]), and glutamate-oxalacetate transaminase is increased three-fold in the Morris 5123 hepatoma[88]. However, in transplanted lymphosarcomas Kit[29] found transaminase activities to be of the same order as in lymphatic tissues; he attributed the low level of aspartate in the lymphosarcomas to rapid utilization rather than impaired formation. Data reported by Blecher & White in 1958[61] indicate much higher activity of aspartate-oxoglutarate transaminase in a lymphosarcoma than in host thymus.

There is a need for closer study of transaminases in the light of recent evidence that each activity is due to two or more enzymes differing, for example, in requirement for pyridoxal phosphate[9] and (at least for glutamate-oxalacetate transaminase) in the nature of the protein. There is already a report[205] of a selective decrease in the mitochondrial glutamate-pyruvate transaminase in the Novikoff hepatoma. Angeletti and co-workers[139] found that one of the glutamate-oxalacetate transaminase peaks present in chromatograms of muscle proteins was lacking in a rhabdosarcoma.

In studies of the fate of injected pyruvate (Chapter 5; Busch[14] & Muramatsu[142]), amino acids such as aspartate were among the products examined. Little radioactivity was recovered in amino acids in the tumours. However, no conclusion concerning the endogenous synthesis of amino acids by transaminations can safely be drawn from the data presented (cf. Chapter 2, last section), or from the decreases observed in the actual amounts of endogenous alanine, aspartate and glutamate.

Glutamine is a versatile compound, being a precursor of protein glutamine and having other important functions, for example in the formation of cytidine nucleotides (from uridine nucleotides) and of NAD (from deamido-NAD). As already mentioned, tumours may be deficient in glutamine, although slow-growing hepatomas await study.

Evidence of impaired conversion of glutamate to glutamine in a mouse hepatoma was obtained in Chaikoff's laboratory[51] (see also G. W. Brown *et al.*, 1956[45]), from experiments in which slices were incubated with labelled glucose or octanoate (the impairment being apparently small with acetate). Enzymic assays have indeed suggested slower synthesis of glutamine from glutamate in Novikoff hepatomas (compared with host liver; V. H. Auerbach & H. A. Waisman, 1954[9,45]), but other hepatomas have shown variable activity (high or low), unrelated to histological appearance (L. Levintow, 1954[45]).

Glutaminase activity is not strikingly altered in precancerous liver or hepatomas[41], although it falls during epidermal carcinogenesis[125]. Apart from the glutaminase pathway for glutamine catabolism, there might be a pathway leading to urea (see Urea synthesis, above). Further study of glutamine metabolism is definitely warranted.

Protein Synthesis

As yet there has been no study of sufficient range and subtlety to delineate the behaviour of protein synthesis in cancerous or precancerous cells. At least it can now be concluded that if plasma proteins are utilized for synthesis of tumour proteins, breakdown to free amino acids first occurs (H. Busch[14], P. N. Campbell[41]).

Whole-animal experiments. With reservations as indicated in the last section of Chapter 2, it can be guessed from measurements of protein labelling after injection of labelled amino acids[41,144,163] that protein synthesis is somewhat depressed in precancerous liver — although ethionine feeding may not give a sustained depression[182] — but almost normal in primary hepatomas. Zamecnik and collaborators in 1952[2] clearly showed that the central portion of a hepatoma is particularly inaccessible to injected amino acids; but from one experiment in which acid-soluble radioactivity was determined, it would appear that hepatomas *in situ* may be quite efficient in incorporating an amino acid into protein once it has entered the cell. A parallelism between amino-acid incorporation into protein and the actual uptake of the amino acid into the cells was noted in a comparison of a mouse hepatoma, normal liver and regenerating liver[153]. The precaution of measuring the intracellular radioactivity of the precursor amino acid was taken in studies which showed depressed incorporation into liver protein following a dose of dimethylnitrosamine (P. N. Magee[11,19]).

Different intracellular elements of cancerous and homologous normal tissues have been little studied with respect to amino-acid incorporation *in vivo*. In rats briefly treated with thioacetamide — an agent which may produce cholangiomas rather than hepatomas — there was increased incorporation of injected lysine into liver protein, especially nuclear histones and supernatant-fraction proteins[53]. Regenerating liver showed a different pattern, the rise in cytoplasmic labelling being more marked for the mitochondrial than for the supernatant fraction. The reduction in cytoplasmic incorporation of leucine found after azo-dye feeding was particularly notable in the microsomal fraction[163].

Whereas a transplanted hepatoma (mouse) studied by a Moscow group[212] showed reduced amino-acid incorporation into nuclear proteins, a transplanted hepatoma (rat) studied in J. L. Irvin's laboratory[16] showed particularly rapid incorporation of glycine into nuclear histone fraction. The generalization has prematurely been made[16a] that neoplasia entails increased synthesis of histones (as distinct from acidic nuclear proteins).

Experiments with intact-cell preparations. With perfused liver from rats fed hepatocarcinogens (usually beyond the critical point as defined in Chapter 1), W. T. Burke & L. L. Miller[41,45] have found increased incorporation of amino acids into plasma and liver proteins; moreover, there was no impairment of the mysterious stimulation normally elicited by adding glutamine to the perfusate. Increased amino-acid incorporation after azo-dye feeding was likewise observed with perfused liver by A. H. Gordon[98], but in contrast with plasma albumin, certain globulins (transferrins and fibrin) showed no increase in labelling (cf. the differential effect on the actual pattern of plasma proteins in perfusates[69]).

Tissue-slice experiments in the laboratories of P. C. Zamecnik[41] and of P. N. Campbell[41] showed increased amino-acid incorporation with liver tumours; but in those studied by Campbell, which were mainly cholangiomas, only the nuclear fraction (crude) showed the increase, and albumin actually showed a decrease. More recently, various transplanted hepatomas have been shown to resemble liver in failing to incorporate valine anaerobically into liver protein, but to surpass liver in aerobic incorporation[6,199]; the acceleration was greatest with fast-growing hepatomas, for which the rate surpassed that found in regenerating liver — a faster-growing tissue than any tumour.

In agreement with observations reported by S. Kit & E. S. G. Barron in 1953[61], intact lymphosarcoma cells were inferior to normal lymphatic cells with respect to amino-acid incorporation into protein *in vitro* under aerobic conditions[61]. Anaerobically, however, the incorporation was high with the lymphosarcoma cells but negligible with the normal cells. These differences may well have been secondary to differences in the rates of respiration and of anaerobic glycolysis. In 1958, J. H. Quastel & I. J. Bickis[6] reported similar observations for anaerobic incorporation in the Novikoff hepatoma compared with liver; aerobically, however, the hepatoma still surpassed liver, as for the hepatomas already mentioned.

In summary, these few intact-cell studies indicate that, under aerobic conditions, hepatomas or precancerous liver generally show increased amino-acid incorporation at least into certain protein fractions. This situation may not be found in tumours other than hepatomas, nor do tumours necessarily show increased anaerobic incorporation. The few results so far obtained *in vivo* (see above) or with cell-free preparations are not fully in accord with these tentative conclusions.

Experiments with cell-free preparations. In suitably supplemented systems from normal liver, microsomes or ribosomes show amino-acid incorporation which is particularly marked with short periods of incubation (although slower than found *in vivo* or with slices), and nuclei and mitochondria each have slight but definite activity. Early work by A. Cantarow and collaborators[41] which indicated an eventual rise, with acetylaminofluorene feeding, in incorporation by mitochondrial fractions warrants repetition and extension. Work with nuclei (K. R. Rees[19]), which indicated that incorporation may be impaired in precancerous liver, likewise needs repetition with particular attention to the purity of the nuclei and to the adequacy of the incubation medium. The same remarks apply to the finding[197] that nuclei from Novikoff hepatomas but not from liver showed amino-acid incorporation into protein.

Assays with microsomal fractions have shown depressed incorporation for hepatomas (of fast growth rate) but not for precancerous liver[41]. When, however, H. T. Shigeura & C. N. Gordon[45] assayed Novikoff hepatomas shortly after intraperitoneal transplantation, the initial as distinct from the overall extent of incorporation surpassed that of regenerating liver if expressed per unit of microsomal protein, and surpassed that of normal liver even if expressed on a fresh-tissue basis; with the hepatomas the incorporation was mainly into non-ribosomal protein.

After ethionine injection there is impairment of incorporation by ribosomes[22,91,144] which, however, was considered to be secondary to "trapping" of ATP by ethionine[91] (see also Chapter 7, Nucleic-acid Synthesis; and Chapter 8, Fig. 12). In general, effects of single doses of hepatocarcinogens — sometimes stimulatory, sometimes inhibitory — as seen also in the laboratories of T. Hultin (see Magee[11,19]) and A. O. Hawtrey[106] — are of uncertain relevance to carcinogenesis, but at least emphasize the complexities that may be encountered in assessing the behaviour of protein synthesis in carcinogenesis.

Little clarification can be expected until more detailed studies are made, which in the case of cell-free systems should take account of recent knowledge in areas such as "messenger RNA" (see Fig. 14, end of Chapter 8, and ref. 18a) and the association of the latter with ribosomes to form "polysomes" (polyribosomes, ergosomes). There is already evidence for disaggregation of polysomes in Novikoff and "minimum-deviation" hepatomas[200] (cf. Shigeura and Gordon[45]) or in liver after administration of ethionine[91]. The supplementation of ribosomes with RNA from a source such as liver or tumour nuclei gave enhanced amino-acid incorporation in the case of an ascitic Novikoff hepatoma[150] (see, however, Shigeura & Gordon[45]); but ribosomes from other hepatomas have yet to be examined by this useful approach. Some evidence of ribosomal derangement has been obtained by electron microscopy (Chapter 1).

Amino-acid activation is perhaps less worthy of attention; it was depressed in a hepatoma and certain other tumours, although probably not sufficiently to render the process rate-limiting[84], but was undiminished in Novikoff hepatomas[80] (cf. Shigeura & Gordon[45]). Ethionine injection possibly impairs the process[144], and "carcinolipin" (a supposed "endogenous" carcinogen) is said to stimulate it when added *in vitro* (J. Hradec[32]).

Amino-acid incorporation into protein merely represents a facet of the protein synthesis; other facets include the tailoring of polypeptide chains into complete proteins, and transfer of the latter to their destination. Phospholipids perhaps play a role[38]. Carcinogenesis might affect one or more of the various stages at least indirectly, and might affect different proteins differently. The few observations already mentioned for individual proteins are compatible with the possibility that in hepatomas there is accelerated production of proteins necessary for cell division and reduced production of non-essential proteins such as serum albumin. Observations bearing on the turnover of "messenger RNA" are considered in Chapters 7 and 8; the suggestion that its output is limited by the ATP level[91] is implausible. Studies of protein synthesis in cancer have sadly lagged behind the rapidly advancing delineation of mechanisms of protein synthesis in normal cells, although much has yet to be learnt about the normal pathways and their control.

CHAPTER 7

Nucleic-Acid Metabolism

FOR convenience in surveying the wide area of nucleic-acid metabolism, consideration will be given firstly to DNA and its catabolism and to acid-soluble 5′-deoxyribonucleotides, and secondly to RNA and its catabolism (including that of the 2′- or 3′-ribonucleotides which are formed, in undetectable amount, during RNA breakdown). Attention will then be given to the supply of 5′-ribonucleotides requisite not only for RNA synthesis (from nucleoside 5′-triphosphates) but also for certain other metabolic processes. Lastly, nucleic-acid synthesis will be considered.

DNA and Its Catabolism

Although the DNA concentration may be subnormal in epidermal carcinomas[17], a rise in the amount of DNA per gram is usually evident in tumours, for example hepatomas[41,199], and is often evident in precancerous liver[41,171]. This rise is not invariably due to a fall in cell size with carcinogenesis; there may, for example, be infiltration of small non-tumour cells such as leucocytes, or aberrations such as increased ploidy in the actual tumour cells[41] (cf. Stich[1]). Accordingly, as already emphasized (Chapter 2), it may be unprofitable to take DNA (or cell number) as the denominator for expressing biochemical results.

R. Daoust[1] has adduced histochemical evidence that the DNA of precancerous or cancerous liver cells is in part located in the cytoplasm. Early biochemical observations from the Millers' laboratory[41] similarly gave evidence of cytoplasmic DNA (in azo-dye hepatomas, but not in precancerous liver), as confirmed by G. C. Hartman (unpublished); but this result could be artefactual.

Alterations in DNA properties. The DNA of primary hepatomas, like the RNA (see below), was found in A. C. Griffin's laboratory to have an elevated guanine content; but E. E. Polli[154] found no such abnormality in DNA from leukaemic leucocytes. However, Polli and collaborators[154] found abnormal features, for example in titration behaviour, in leucocyte DNA from myeloid-leukaemia patients compared with lymphatic-leukaemia patients or normal humans. Chromatographic fractionation of the DNA from various transplanted tumours, as performed in the laboratory of S. Kit[7,117], showed no gross abnormalities in elution profile. However, there may be chromatographic differences in DNA between lymphosarcoma (primary) and thymus[185], and metabolic differences (see below) between liver and hepatoma[134]. Moreover, DNA preparations from leukaemic leucocytes, normal leucocytes and spleen have been found to differ from each other in chromatographic profile (Bendich and collaborators[86,*185*]), and in sedimentation behaviour[154].

Apparent differences in DNA among normal tissues — as also observed in a comparison of brain and kidney in Bendich's laboratory[*154*] — are evidently a complication, possibly meaningful in terms of "endogenous" minor components associated with DNA, but more probably attributable to DNAase action or other *in vitro* artefacts. K. S. Kirby[8] has noted the presence of a small amount of protein (not histone) in samples of purified DNA, but his data do not establish any definite change with carcinogenesis in the amount of this protein. Other evidence points to a high content of histone in the DNA of tumour cells[103]. There is histochemical evidence for abnormal staining — apparently due to firm bonding between histone and DNA — in nuclei of tumours provided that these are malignant (O. S. Frankfurt[31]).

More subtle studies of tumours must, in line with remarks by V. S. Shapot[32], await the development of better methods for the isolation of DNA, for its examination by chromatographic or other procedures, and for the assessment of the extent to which the fractionation of DNA is affected by substances associated with the "purified" DNA (as adventitious contaminants?).

Deoxyribonucleases. Acid DNAase ("DNAase II") is mainly present in lysosomes, in bound form, but significant activity has also been found in purified nuclei (from liver) and in supernatant fractions. The activity of the latter, possibly arising by rupture of fragile digestive bodies such as phagosomes (Chapter 1, Electron Microscopy), is conceivably a determinant of the rate of DNA catabolism *in vivo.* Alkaline DNAase ("neutral DNAase", "DNAase I"), which gives rise to 5′- rather than to 3′-dexoyribonucleotides, occurs mainly in mitochondria and to a small extent in nuclei; but activity is normally masked by an endogenous inhibitor. Excusable lack of awareness of these complexities mars early work[25] on nucleases in tumours. Although the view has been expressed that DNAase activity in tumours is similar to that in other rapidly proliferating tissues[59], there is a need for closer study, particularly since there are scattered observations which suggest that a rise in DNAase may foreshadow DNA synthesis in normal cells — perhaps through despiralization or disjunction of DNA double strands (Shapot[32]).

From the few observations for acid DNAase[41] it appears that "total" activity tends to be low in primary hepatomas — although a rise was reported by Maver and Greco in 1956[136] for transplanted hepatomas — but that supernatant-fraction activity is high in hepatomas and also in precancerous liver. In the light of a report by G. de Lamirande and collaborators in 1953[41], concerning increased activity in crude nuclear fractions from hepatomas, purified nuclei have been studied by G. C. Hartman in the author's laboratory but have shown no striking rise in activity.

Histochemical tests — which may well be more open to artefacts than biochemical assays — have shown no activity of acid DNAase in the nuclei of Novikoff hepatomas, and reduced activity in cytoplasmic granules[198]. DNAase activity as examined histochemically by Daoust[1], at a pH near neutrality, was apparently absent from actual neoplastic cells in azo-dye hepatoma nodules. Daoust has suggested that loss of nuclease activity is an important step in carcinogenesis, enabling foreign or abnormal nucleic acids to become incorporated into the genetic material of the cell. Alkaline DNAase has not yet been studied biochemically in relation to carcinogenesis.

5′-Deoxyribonucleotides*

The levels of acid-soluble 5′-deoxyribonucleotides in liver are extremely low, even in comparison with those of cytidine nucleotides (of which mention will be made later). It has been suggested that the rate of DNA synthesis is determined by the supply of deoxyribonucleotide triphosphates, perhaps dTTP (TTP) in particular (Roth[168], Smellie[16,16a], Shapot[32], *inter alia*). Evidence concerning neoplasia, now to be considered, points to a faster supply

Tissue levels. By microbiological assays which differentiated deoxyribonucleotides from deoxynucleosides but not from one another, it was shown in W. C. Schneider's laboratory[16] that in normal liver the main deoxyribosyl constituent is deoxycytidine, whereas in the Novikoff hepatoma and in regenerating liver there is an enlarged pool (per gram) of deoxyribonucleotides (including di- and/or triphosphates) but not of deoxycytidine. The deoxyribosyl pool in nuclei isolated in non-aqueous media represented as much as half of the whole-tissue pool, and its relative amount was unchanged in the hepatomas — as was the actual size of the pool if calculated on the basis of DNA rather than tissue weight.

5′-Deoxyribonucleotide metabolism. The levels of deoxyribonucleotides depend upon the balance among various anabolic

* The numeral specifies not the deoxy position but that of the phosphate. Some authors use the deplorable term "deoxynucleotides". In connexion with the standard abbreviations now employed — the isomers being 5′ unless otherwise stated — it should be noted that many authors omit the prefix "d" (or use "de") before TMP, TDP and TTP.

and catabolic reactions[168]. A decreased capacity for the dephosphorylation of deoxyribonucleotides was observed in S. Fiala's laboratory[41] for primary or Novikoff hepatomas, and also (on the basis of DNA rather than tissue weight) for liver late during azo-dye feeding. Particular attention was paid to a supposed "dCMPase" (really a non-specific phosphatase?), but no attention to the question of latency. However, it appears from observations on Morris 5123 hepatomas in F. Maley's laboratory[133] that decreased dCMPase activity is not a minimum deviation. According to Roth[47], dTMPase was increased in a range of hepatomas, roughly in proportion to their growth rate.

In 1961 Fiala and Kasinsky[41] stated that, on a weight basis, the Novikoff hepatoma is more active than liver in deaminating deoxyadenosine; but the data in the paper itself seem to refute this conclusion. The deamination of deoxyribonucleosides has also been studied in Roth's laboratory[168]; with deoxyguanosine as substrate the activity (per gram) was high in the Dunning hepatoma, normal in the Morris 5123, and low in the Novikoff, but with deoxyadenosine the activity was near normal in each hepatoma.

Hepatomas including the Morris 5123 have shown somewhat low levels of thymidine phosphorylase activity[216]. Thymine reductase, which is probably the rate-limiting step in thymine catabolism, was low in hepatomas studied in P. Emmelot's laboratory[105], but almost normal in some of the hepatomas studied by V. R. Potter *et al.*[8,155].

With two reservations — that direct conversion of UMP into dUMP may be only a minor pathway in liver, and that conversion of CMP into dCMP apparently occurs at the diphosphate level — the scheme on the facing page may be helpful in considering the supply of dTTP.

The scanty evidence on CMP formation in neoplasia will be considered later in connection with 5′-ribonucleotides. The overall process denoted *1*, as studied by E. C. Moore & R. B. Hurlbert[123], is demonstrable with Novikoff hepatomas but not with liver. Reactions analogous to *1* have been shown for adenosine, guanosine and uridine nucleotides[123], and require as co-factor an —S—S— protein, "thioredoxine" (P. Reichard, 1964) rather than lipoate as was originally supposed.

Reaction *2*, apparently representing the main pathway for dUMP formation and mediated by dCMP aminohydrolase (deaminase), has been studied by various authors[105], the literature being notable for controversy rather than clarity. Almost the only point on which there is agreement is that activity is high in rapidly growing tissues, including regenerating liver, Novikoff hepatomas, and primary hepatomas induced by azo dyes or ethionine. With conventional biochemical assays, as distinct from assays with radioactive dCMP, measurable activity in normal liver has been

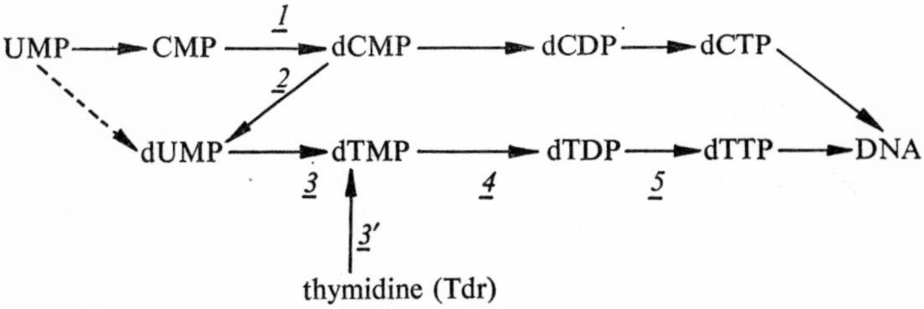

reported only by certain authors such as S. Fiala. His data hardly establish his claim to have found good activity; moreover, the notably high activity stated by J. S. Roth *et al.*[105,169] to be demonstrable with modified assay conditions does not fully accord with the data actually presented, and has not been confirmed[105].

For reaction *2*, slow-growing hepatomas such as the Morris 5123 show activity close to that of normal liver, according to Pitot[37] (Fig. 10), Maley[133] and Roth[168]. Evidence from Fiala's laboratory that the activity of the Dunning hepatoma is higher than was previously supposed is hardly conclusive. Although it is agreed that fast-growing hepatomas usually have high activity, P. Emmelot and co-workers[105] found no clear correlation between growth rate and activity in a range of hepatomas.

On the grounds of high activity found simultaneously with bile-duct proliferation during azo-dye feeding[37], Potter[8] speculated that the enzyme in normal liver is confined to bile-duct cells, the dUMP (or deoxyuridine) being transferred to parenchymal cells for dTMP synthesis, and that "hepatomas" high in dCMP

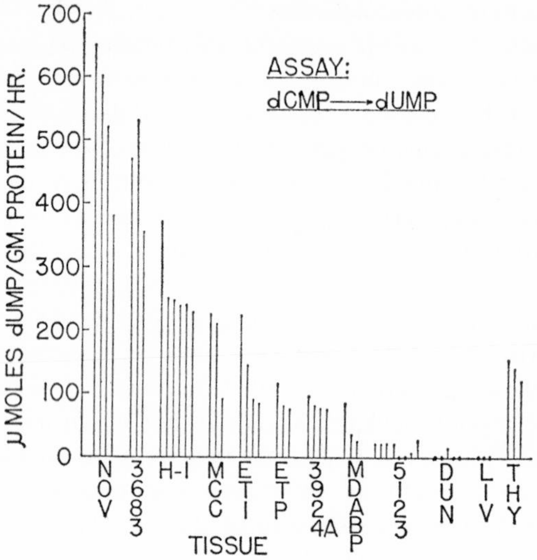

FIG. 10. dCMP aminohydrolase (deaminase) activity of eleven hepatomas and of liver and thymus in the rat (V. R. Potter *et al.*[155]). Each vertical line or point represents one animal. NOV = Novikoff hepatoma, 3683 = Morris hepatoma 3683, H–I = ethionine-induced hepatoma passed through tissue-culture, MCC = McCoy hepatoma; ETI = first- and second-generation transplants of: ETP = primary hepatomas induced by ethionine; 3924A = Morris hepatoma 3924A, MDABP = primary hepatomas induced by 4-dimethylamino-3′-methylaminoazobenzene (3′-Me-DAB), 5123 = Morris hepatoma 5123, DUN = Dunning L-C18 hepatoma LIV = liver, THY = thymus. Note that thymus, which synthesizes DNA rapidly, has high activity.

aminohydrolase activity (but low in enzymes such as glucose-6-phosphatase, which is absent from bile-duct cells) really originated from bile-duct cells. This speculation, already questioned by Emmelot[32] and by Fiala (see also Roth[168,169]), was undermined by the inability of Hartman & Reid[105] to show a rise either with an azo dye or with α-naphthylisothiocyanate[105] — the latter causing especially marked bile-duct proliferation (Plate 2b, Chapter 1). At least it is unlikely that a rise in dCMP aminohydrolase is crucial for carcinogenesis, particularly since normal and leukaemic leucocytes have similar activities[183].

The synthesis of dTMP is conceivably limited not by reaction *2* in the above scheme, but — at least in leucocytes (F. M. Huennekens[16]; cf. Davidson[8]) — by reaction *3* catalysed by "thymidylate synthetase". This enzyme, assayed in the laboratories of C. Heidelberger[105a] and F. Maley[133] with addition of the co-factor (tetrahydrofolate, THFA[36]), has not been detected in liver but is high in primary or transplanted hepatomas — particularly high in the Novikoff hepatoma but quite high even in the Morris 5123 hepatoma. Precancerous or regenerating liver has likewise shown high activity. Leucocytes normally have no detectable activity, but may show high activity in acute leukaemia and, more notably, in chronic myeloid leukaemia, though not in chronic lymphoid leukaemia[183]; however, such a rise in activity (as also found in a non-malignant condition, infectious mononucleosis) was considered to be merely a reflection of the high DNA-synthesizing capacity of immature cells[183].

The rate of formation of dTMP might be determined not by thymidylate synthetase itself but — at least in tissues other than liver (Werkheiser[3]) — by the supply of THFA, and in particular by the reductase which catalyses THFA formation from dihydrofolate[36]. Reductase activity was somewhat low in certain tumours (including azo dye hepatomas) although high in regenerating liver (B. M. Braganca & V. W. Kenkare[32]). However, in agreement with W. Wilmans (1961), R. Silber and collaborators[183] (see also Bertino[3]) found reductase activity to be high in leucocytes in acute or chronic myeloid leukaemia, but hardly detectable in normal humans or in chronic lymphatic leukaemia. The formate-activating enzyme, THFA formylase, was high in the latter condition and also, according to Wilmans, in myeloid leukaemia (acute or chronic)[36,183]. V. Mitbander and collaborators reported in 1962[161] that azo-dye hepatomas are very low in "citrovorum factor" (5-formyl-THFA); but their data do not seem to bear out their further statement that hepatomas have little capacity to convert folate (pteroylglutamate) into citrovorum factor *in vitro*.

The reaction denoted *3′* in the foregoing scheme is catalysed by thymidine kinase (or kinases[66]), and is of uncertain importance in normal tissues — possibly less important in the human than in the mouse[60]. Bianchi[4,60] found high activity in leukaemic tissues (mouse), in leucocytes from certain leukaemic patients, and in a rat hepatoma (compared with liver; unpublished observation). In a range of hepatomas, Roth[47] found that the activity was well correlated with growth rate.

The conversion of dTMP into dTTP (reactions *4* and *5* in the foregoing scheme; via dTDP — see R. M. S. Smellie[16]) is unlikely to be rate-limiting in DNA synthesis. High values for the kinase activity in cell-free preparations have been found for an ascitic hepatoma[117] and for solid hepatomas — the slow-growing Morris 5123 hepatoma showing particularly high activity (Roth[47]). However, the low activity found for liver appeared to be due not to lack of enzyme but to interfering reactions[117]; a similar explanation was suggested for the further observation that the rate of formation of dCTP from dCMP was low in the ascitic hepatoma as compared with liver[117].

For deoxyribonucleotide synthesis there might be an alternative pathway — of uncertain importance in mammalian tissues — starting from deoxyribose phosphate. The aldolase concerned in the synthesis of deoxyribose phosphate from glyceraldehyde-3-phosphate and acetaldehyde was reported by G. E. Boxer and C. E. Shonk in 1958[14,41] to show high activity in hepatomas (or in regenerating liver); moreover, there was slower breakdown of deoxyribose phosphate.

RNA and Its Catabolism

Tumours often[25,171] but not invariably[185] show a decreased ratio of RNA to DNA, but there is not necessarily a fall in the absolute amount of RNA per gram. Indeed, it appears from data given by L. Ledoux and co-workers for human cervical epithelium that the content of RNA (per unit of protein) tended to be higher in malignant portions than in non-malignant portions, although the normal scatter of values was wide. It is, however, unprofitable merely to measure RNA in whole tissues. Although more than half of the RNA in liver is microsomal — largely ribosomal, but probably within the cytomembranes also — the supernatant fraction contains diverse species of "transfer RNA"; moreover, mitochondria and nuclei each contain a small amount of RNA (itself heterogeneous at least in the case of nuclei[14,33]) quite apart from the RNA commonly present because of microsomal contamination.

RNA levels in sub-cellular fractions. Most published results for "nuclear" and "mitochondrial" RNA — one trend being a fall in mitochondrial-fraction RNA with hepatocarcinogenesis[12,41,163] — are of doubtful interpretation, for the reason just indicated. The average content of RNA in carefully purified nuclei may be unchanged relative to DNA but at least is increased per gram of whole tissue, as shown by Y. Moulé and J. Chauveau in 1959[12,41] for hepatomas, by M. K. Turner (unpublished experiments) for hepatomas and for liver from rats given azo dyes, and by H. Busch and collaborators[53,14] for liver from rats given thioacetamide (which, according to Grant and Rees[41,109], produces cholangiomas). With ethionine feeding there is a rise in nuclear RNA even relative to DNA[196], perhaps linked with the increase in number of nucleoli. In a study with transplanted hepatomas (mouse)[174], nuclear RNA likewise appeared to be increased relative to DNA, although not relative to nuclear protein, and there tended to be a higher proportion of RNA associated with "acid protein" as distinct from a "nucleoprotein" fraction containing DNA. Rat hepatomas, but not precancerous liver, have also shown a rise in nuclear RNA relative to DNA[202].

Nuclear RNA needs much closer study, with especial regard to two possibilities: that in preparing purified nuclei there may be unintended selection from a metabolically heterogeneous cell population (see Chapter 2, Experiments with cell-free preparations), and that a particular species of nuclear RNA may be disproportionately affected by carcinogenesis (cf. 212). In the above experiments with thioacetamide, nucleolar RNA showed a particularly striking increase. No such disproportionate increase in nucleolar RNA was found with an ascitic hepatoma (P. Mandel *et al.*, 1963[33]); there was, however, a notably high content of RNA in the nuclear sap (containing nuclear ribosomes) and a decreased proportion of DNA-linked ("messenger"?) RNA.

A fall in microsomal RNA is a particularly consistent feature of hepatocarcinogenesis, and possibly of carcinogenesis in general (although data such as A. Laird has adduced are vitiated by lack of a normal-tissue baseline). The fall is found quite early during feeding with hepatocarcinogens[14,41] — ethionine being a notable exception (E. Reid, unpublished) — and is evident even in the Morris 5123 hepatoma[163].

The apparent fall in microsomal RNA could in part be due to the detachment of ribosomes from cytomembranes that is evident by electron microscopy (Chapter 1), and to break-up of polysomes[200]. Free ribosomes would not be efficiently sedimented with centrifugal forces of the order of 20,000 *g*, as used in some laboratories (such as that of the author) for routine preparation of microsomes. However, detachment of ribosomes could not be the sole cause of the fall in microsomal RNA, since supernatant-fraction RNA does not sharply rise in hepatocarcinogenesis[41]. Probably there is actual breakdown of RNA, perhaps analogous to that demonstrated by R. Tsanev (see p. 69, in ref. 19) in epidermal cells following mechanical injury. The RNA which is lost from microsomes in hepatocarcinogenesis may come partly from the actual cytomembranes — a possibility compatible with early ultra-centrifugal observations from M. L. Peterman's laboratory[41] — but at least some of it probably comes from ribosomes[41]. Evidence that hepatoma ribosomes are *more* stable than normal[204] is hardly conclusive.

Further work on RNA in different sub-cellular fractions will be of little value unless individual species or classes of RNA are investigated, preferably in conjunction with isotopic techniques and with electron microscopy. A few attempts have already been made to ascertain whether carcinogenesis entails subtle changes in certain properties of RNA, although few techniques are so far available.

Alterations in RNA properties. Differences in the chromatographic behaviour of RNA between the Novikoff hepatoma and liver have been observed for nuclear, microsomal and post-microsomal fractions, but not for supernatant fractions[80]; the results could, however, have been largely a reflection of less ready sedimentation of ribosomes in the hepatoma. More conclusive evidence of altered chromatographic behaviour of RNA has been obtained with lymphosarcomas induced in mouse thymus by X-irradiation[185]. Since, however, the "abnormal" pattern was likewise observed with thymus from newborn mice, the pattern was felt to be merely a manifestation of rapid growth or of cell immaturity[185]. Hepatoma RNA examined by counter-current distribution appears to be abnormal in respect of "rapidly labelled" (messenger?) RNA, although not of ribosomal RNA[116].

Determination of RNA base composition have shown a rise in guanine in primary hepatomas as studied by G. de Lamirande and collaborators[41] (*inter alia*), and in various transplanted tumours compared with a range of normal tissues[25]. Among the sub-cellular fractions isolated from the primary hepatomas, the microsomal fraction was exceptional in not showing increased guanine. Reid[163] found that supernatant-fraction RNA had increased guanine in Morris 5123 hepatomas as well as in primary hepatomas. The rise is a relatively late event in azo-dye carcinogenesis[163,171]. It would be of interest to know whether the rise is confined to particular species of RNA, and also whether there are altered amounts of "abnormal" bases such as are present in the "transfer RNA" of supernatant fractions.

Ribonucleases. Like acid DNAase, acid RNAase is located mainly in lysosomes; but some activity, conceivably of special metabolic significance, is also found in nuclei and in supernatant fractions. Alkaline RNAase is partly bound in particles — possibly akin to, if not idential with, lysosomes — but is also found to a notable extent in supernatant fractions, albeit accompanied by an inhibitor. Latent activity, of low extent, has also been reported for ribosomes, and has been thought to play some role in protein synthesis. A possible role of RNAases in nuclei and in ribosomes is to destroy unwanted "templates" (I. Leslie[1]). There may, however, be a broader function (as suggested by Reid[41,163] for the acid RNAase of the supernatant fraction), in offsetting or even triggering off a rise in the rate of synthesis of RNA in microsomes or other loci; "template" RNA probably represents only a fraction (1% ?) of the total RNA of the cell. Liver RNAases ultimately break RNA down to cyclic mononucleotides (phosphate bridge across 2′ and 3′), only pyrimidine in the case of alkaline RNAase; the conversion of the cyclic nucleotides into straight-chain nucleotides (e.g. 2′-AMP, 3′-UMP) is catalysed by distinct diesterases. The latter enzymes are unlikely to be rate-limiting, and show only minor changes in activity with hepatocarcinogenesis (J. T. Nodes and E. Reid, 1963[163]).

The early oncological work on RNAases, like that on DNAases, is uninformative because the complexities indicated above were overlooked. More recent reports from various laboratories have shown[41,163,169] that it is difficult to generalize about changes with hepatocarcinogenesis. Reports in 1956 and 1962 by Maver and Greco[136] indicated that the values for alkaline RNAase (without destruction of the inhibitor) and for acid RNAase in transplanted hepatomas may range from high to low compared with liver. Amongst the Novikoff hepatomas studied by C. Allard and collaborators[41,45] — the inhibitor being apparently inoperative in their assays — some showed normal activity for alkaline RNAase and others very high activity. From assays in which the inhibitor was deliberately destroyed, alkaline-RNAase activity in homogenates or sub-cellular fractions has been variously reported as low, normal, and (in some "minimum-deviation" hepatomas) high[41,169]. J. S. Roth[41,169] further showed that the amount of inhibitor is high in rats fed acetylaminofluorene (whereas the enzyme, assayed in mitochondrial fractions, is decreased), but is usually low in hepatomas including the Novikoff hepatoma.

Acid RNAase as assayed in lysosome-containing fractions (with prior liberation of latent activity) is little changed in precancerous liver but somewhat decreased in hepatomas[41]. Purified nuclei from hepatomas show activity of the normal order (M. K. Turner, unpublished). For the activity in supernatant fractions, as studied particularly in the laboratories of E. Reid[41,163] and J. S. Roth[169], a dramatic rise has been found in precancerous liver even with ethionine (but likewise with α-naphthylisothiocyanate, which is non-carcinogenic). An even more dramatic rise is usually evident with supernatants from hepatomas, including slow-growing (minimum-deviation) hepatomas but with one unexplained exception amongst primary hepatomas — those designated "small-celled adenocarcinomas", in which J. T. Nodes and E. Reid[163] found no rise. No rise of supernatant-fraction activity occurs in regenerating liver[41]. Actinomycin D sometimes reduces the rise in precancerous liver (A. B. El-Aaser & E. Reid).

Increased activity of acid RNAase in supernatant fractions could conceivably be an artefact due to increased fragility of primary lysosomes. From trial of mild conditions for homogenization, Reid and Nodes concluded in 1963[163] that this is an unlikely explanation. If the activity arises by rupture of autophagic vacuoles or similar organelles (Fig. 2, Chapter 1), the increased activity would in one sense be an artefact, but might nevertheless have significance in relation to RNA catabolism *in vivo*, and accord with a recent speculation that lysosomes are the primary target for carcinogens[55]. At present it seems unlikely that necrotic cells or non-parenchymal cells (such as bile-duct or Kupffer cells) are the main locus of the high activity. There is indeed an increase in supernatant-fraction activity after pedicle ligation (de Duve[19]), but necrosis thus produced might differ in character from that found in hepatomas. Ingenious histochemical studies by H. Amano & R. Daoust[1] represent a useful approach, and did in fact show notably high RNAase activity in the necrotic regions of hepatomas; but the results hardly help in the interpretation of the rise in supernatant-fraction acid RNAase, since the assays were at a neutral pH and since it is not clear to what extent latent (lysosomal) activity was liberated. Mention has already been made, in connection with DNAases, of Daoust's speculation concerning loss of nucleases with carcinogenesis.

There is little information for cancer in sites other than the liver. L. Ledoux and colleagues[123] studied acid RNAase (presumably "total") in normal and cancerous epithelium from human uterine cervix. Activity was low in the cancerous tissue, the samples of which showed a positive correlation between acid-RNAase activity and RNA content. A similar correlation was evident among different normal tissues compared by Ledoux; but the correlation breaks down if comparison is made not amongst cancerous tissues or amongst normal tissues, but between cancerous tissues (or tissues from rats with an endocrine imbalance) and normal tissues.

Catabolism of 2′- and 3′-ribonucleotides. With hepatocarcinogenesis, the catabolism of purine nucleotides formed by breakdown of RNA, as instanced by 2′-AMP, may well be accelerated at least as far as inosine. The enzymic steps concerned are shown in Fig. 11, together with the effects observed in the author's laboratory with azo-dye feeding; Fig. 11 also summarizes results for RNA levels and for RNAases as already discussed, and results for 5′-ribonucleotides to be considered later. The rate of formation of inosine is probably determined not by the non-specific phosphatases which act on the nucleotides, but by adenosine deaminase, the activity of which was found in laboratories other than the author's to be already increased in precancerous liver[41,85].

The rate of catabolism of inosine can hardly be determined by inosine phosphorylase, the activity of which in normal liver is extremely high. However, normal liver shows very low activity for xanthine oxidase, which catalyses the formation of uric acid from hypoxanthine and xanthine (one source of the latter being the

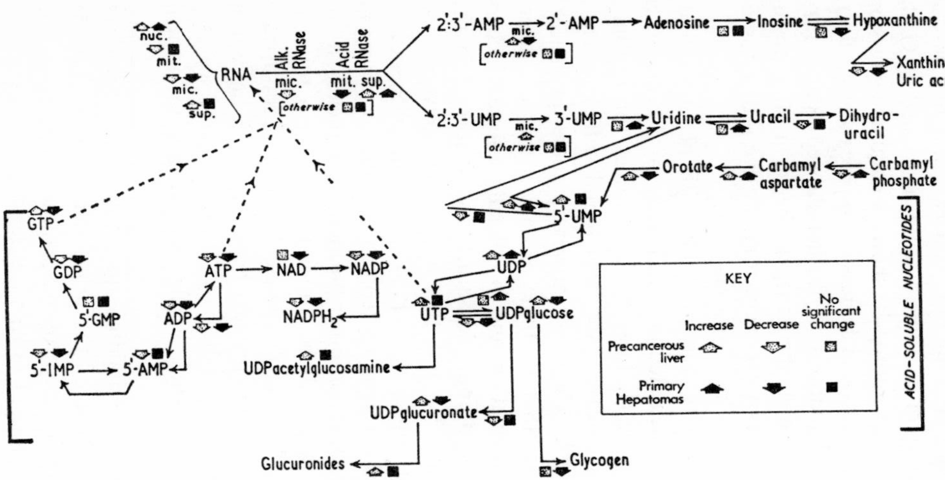

FIG. 11. Levels of RNA and of acid-soluble nucleotides, and activities of enzymes concerned in RNA and nucleotide metabolism: summary of findings with albino rats in the author's laboratory[163] for pre-cancerous liver (3′-Me-DAB, fed for 2–5 weeks) and for primary hepatoma nodules. Changes (per g tissue) in the level of RNA in a cell fraction, or of an acid-soluble nucleotide in whole tissue, are shown *above* the entry for the constituent, and changes (per g tissue) in the activity of an enzyme *in vitro* are shown *below* the arrow for the reaction. Nuc. = purified nuclei (examined only in respect of RNA), mit. = mitochondrial fraction, mic. = microsomal fraction, sup. = supernatant fraction.

guanine which arises — perhaps at a reduced rate in primary hepatomas[41]; cf. ref. 85 — from guanine nucleotides).

The distinction between "xanthine dehydrogenase" (as assayed in some laboratories) and "xanthine oxidase"[9] will not be discussed here. The activity of xanthine oxidase, as studied by G. de Lamirande[85] and by other authors[41], shows a notable depression in primary hepatomas and some depression in precancerous liver. A. Sreenivasan and collaborators[161] further showed that *in vitro* addition of dimethylaminoazobenzene, in the form of a postulated derivative produced by pre-incubating the dye with a homogenate, depressed the activity of normal liver.

Xanthine-oxidase activity falls not only with hepatocarcinogenesis, but also — if calculated on a cell basis — with the onset of breast cancer in mice (I. Lewin[9]). Low values for xanthine oxidase, and also for uricase, have been found with leukaemic lymphocytes (mouse)[92]. There is, however, some evidence[41] against the possibilities that xanthine oxidase is the sole determinant of uric acid formation and is crucially affected in carcinogenesis. Indeed, xanthine-oxidase activity is normal in the Morris 5123 hepatoma[207], and this and other slow-growing hepatomas, studied as minces by G. P. Wheeler and colleagues[203], have shown an actual acceleration (compared with host liver) in the catabolism of xanthine and other purines. Nevertheless, a fall in xanthine oxidase may well be important as a step towards advanced malignancy. This conclusion can hardly hold for uricase (the activity of which is low in primary hepatomas[41,85], but not in Morris 5123 hepatomas as studied by Wheeler *et al.*; see also Novikoff[7]), this enzyme being apparently lacking in normal human tissues.

In the catabolism of pyrimidine nucleotides, an important bottleneck is the reduction of the uracil derived from uridine (Fig. 11). Dihydrouracil dehydrogenase (uracil reductase) has shown activity of the normal order in at least some hepatomas studied in the laboratories of V. R. Potter[8] and E. Reid[163]. A very low rate of uracil degradation was found with slices from a mouse hepatoma[73], but even with liver slices the rate was so low that the limiting factor may well have been the penetration of uracil into the cell. Liver from rats fed azo dyes, carcinogenic or non-carcinogenic, has shown a fall in dihydrouracil-dehydrogenase activity[163] which could contribute to the rise in uridine-nucleotide levels mentioned below — although the levels do not rise with ethionine feeding despite a fall in dehydrogenase activity.

5′-Ribonucleotides

With hepatocarcinogenesis, nicotinamide-adenine dinucleotides ("pyridine nucleotides") show changes in concentration (Chapter 5) which are summarized in Fig. 11 but will not be further discussed here. With the exception of cytidine nucleotides, the amounts of which are very small in normal liver, 5′-ribonucleotides are readily detectable (by anion-exchange chromatography) in the form of mono-, di- and triphosphates (abbreviated MP, DP, and TP). The relative amounts are influenced by the extraction conditions; in an early study by G. A. LePage[41] there was almost complete breakdown of triphosphates, but even with "good" conditions the appearance of mono- and diphosphates is conceivably artefactual.

Tissue levels. With supposedly satisfactory extraction conditions, J. T. Nodes and E. Reid[163] found for primary hepatomas an increased proportion of monophosphates relative to triphosphates. However, with an ascitic hepatoma studied in P. Mandel's laboratory[33] there was a relatively high content of triphosphates (including CTP), as also found for a range of tumours compared with non-homologous normal tissues[177]. If the adenosine, guanosine and uridine series of nucleotides are each considered as a whole, a provisional generalization can be made about hepatomas including the Morris 5123 — that purine as distinct from uridine nucleotides are reduced in concentration. A fall in IMP — which gives rise both to AMP and to GMP in the *de novo* pathway for purine nucleotide biosynthesis — is a particularly early event in azo-dye carcinogenesis (Nodes & Reid[163]).

In liver from rats fed carcinogenic azo dyes, uridine nucleotides have shown a striking rise (Nodes and Reid[163]; Fig. 11); with non-carcinogenic dyes the rise was smaller except for UDPglucuronate. However, dimethylaminoazobenzene, acetylaminofluorene and ethionine as given in A. Rabbi's laboratory[157] did not have this effect and, indeed, markedly depressed the level of UTP and of the other tri-phosphates; the results with ethionine have in part been confirmed in the author's laboratory. A fall in CMP has also been noted[157], contrary to observations for ascitic hepatomas[33].

In hepatomas — primary, Morris 5123, or ascitic — there are low levels of UDPglucose, UDPglucuronate, and sometimes of UDPacetylglucosamine (Nodes & Reid[163], and Mandel and co-workers[33], *inter alia*). Primary hepatomas with a high content of fibrous tissue showed particularly low levels, as if these nucleotides were being diverted into mucopolysaccharide synthesis; but unfortunately for this speculation the fibrous tissue was shown to be of collagenous type[163]. Mandel[33] suggests that there is reduced production of these conjugated nucleotides, related to a lack of polysaccharide-containing membranes in tumour cells.

The above results for nucleotides were obtained with whole tissue. Certain nucleotides, notably adenosine nucleotides, are in part located in mitochondria, as already discussed (Chapter 5). Nuclei resemble whole tissue with respect to the pattern and concentrations of ribonucleotides; there is some evidence for a weak barrier in this respect between nucleus and cytoplasm, but no evidence for a change in this supposed barrier with hepatocarcinogenesis (E. Reid & G. Siebert, unpublished work). Certainly there is no evidence for a critically low level of ATP in nuclei such as might justify certain speculations mentioned in connection with nicotinamide-adenine dinucleotides (Chapter 5) and with protein synthesis (Chapter 6).

5′-Ribonucleotide metabolism. Although Fig. 11 refers merely to findings by the author and collaborators and is not universally valid for hepatocarcinogenesis, it may be taken as a focus for consideration of enzymic changes underlying changes in nucleotide levels. At least it would appear that the primary hepatomas studied were less prone than Morris 5123 hepatomas to show certain abnormalities, such as a fall in the capacity for glucuronide synthesis from UDPglucuronate (cf. Novikoff[7]). The rise in this activity found in precancerous liver (Fig. 11), like the rise in UDPglucuronate level, may be related to disposal of azo-dye metabolites as glucuronides, and is probably irrelevant to carcinogenesis[163] — although increased activity has likewise been found (by G. J. Dutton; see Boyland[21]) in skin treated with benzpyrene. For reactions centered on UDPglucose — its formation, and its conversion into glycogen (Chapter 5) or UDP-glucuronate — Fig. 11 shows certain changes which, however, are probably unimportant[163].

Besides the *de novo* pathway for synthesis of 5′-UMP, there is a "salvage" pathway whereby uridine formed by RNA catabolism can be re-utilized (Fig. 11). The enzyme concerned, uridine kinase, shows higher activity in normal liver than is generally supposed. With the reservation that it is uncertain whether the endogenous level of uridine is high enough to saturate the enzyme, it can be concluded from uridine-kinase assays that the "salvage" pathway operates faster in precancerous liver (with ethionine as well as with carcinogenic azo dyes), in primary hepatomas[163], and also in various human tumours as reported in 1963 by Kara, Sorm and Winkler[*163*]. Whole-animal experiments with labelled uracil by A. Cantarow and co-workers[41], although marred by the use of a vast dose, at least support the view that the capacity of the pathway is increased; moreover, the endogenous supply of uridine from RNA may well be increased as judged by the results for acid RNAase. Since, however, uridine-kinase activity is likewise high in non-cancerous proliferating tissues such as regenerating liver (O. Sköld[9,*163*]) but is normal in the Morris 5123 hepatoma[163], increased activity is best regarded as a forerunner and concomitant of *rapid* tissue growth.

The latter conclusion may also apply to the synthesis of 5′-UMP by the *de novo* pathway from orotate (Fig. 11), this pathway being increased in capacity in precancerous liver (even with ethionine), in primary hepatomas[163], and in leukaemic leucocytes as studied by L. H. Smith and collaborators[163], but not in Morris 5123 hepatomas[163]. The view that there is an increase in capacity holds whether the rate is determined by aspartate transcarbamoylase — this enzyme competing with ornithine transcarbamoylase for the supply of carbamoylphosphate as emphasized by Potter[8] (cf. Chapter 6, Urea synthesis) — or by the "free" activity of the enzyme systems which convert carbamoylaspartate into orotate, as suggested by Reid[41,163]. The enzyme system by which orotate is converted into UMP shows somewhat reduced activity in primary or Morris 5123 hepatomas[163], but is unlikely to be rate-limiting in the synthesis of UMP. Regulation of the whole pathway perhaps depends less on enzyme levels than on feed-back control by end-products such as CTP or UMP itself (Pardee[3]); however, the scanty information available gives no reason to believe that the balance or the actual nature of these controls is abnormal in tumours (cf. Chapter 8).

Even in hepatomas UMP, UDP and UTP appear to be readily interconvertible, although there is a tendency for UTP to be low relative to UDP in azo-dye hepatomas — a tendency which accords with the increased "free" activity of enzyme(s) which dephosphorylate UTP[163] (Fig. 11). It is questionable whether the level of UMP is determined by 5′-nucleotidase, the activity of which in homogenates is not dramatically or consistently changed with hepatocarcinogenesis[85,163]. But this enzyme — which is located not in nuclei and cytomembranes as biochemical literature suggests, but in bile canaliculi, in sinusoids, and in fibrous tissue as found in hepatomas — may nevertheless repay subtle study (cf. J. P. Chang[7,31], A. B. Novikoff[7]). Perhaps the enzyme has a special function in transfer of the nucleoside moiety across the plasma membrane (cf. de Verdier and Potter, 1960[8]).

The later catabolic step mediated by dihydrouracil dehydrogenase may well be a determinant of the UMP level, and the fall in activity already mentioned as occurring in precancerous liver could, in conjunction with faster synthesis of UMP, account for the dramatic rise in UMP level with azo-dye feeding. The lack of a consistent rise in UMP and other uridine nucleotides in rats fed ethionine, and in azo-dye hepatomas, could be due to accelerated utilization for RNA synthesis, as will be discussed later.

For the conversion (apparently at the diphosphate level) of uridine nucleotides into cytidine nucleotides — the latter being so low in amount that they might be rate-limiting in RNA synthesis — there is the isolated but interesting observation[110] that the Novikoff hepatoma, unlike normal liver, has high activity.

Apart from rather uninformative observations on ATPase (Chapter 5) and on 5′-nucleotidase (see above) there are few enzymic observations bearing on the changes in purine nucleotides summarized in Fig. 11, for example the fall in ATP produced by azo-dye feeding (the fall being less marked than with ethionine[91, 182]). The fall in IMP already mentioned suggests a defect in the *de novo* pathway; but no direct information is available for the enzymes concerned, or for the operation in neoplastic tissue of the feed-back controls which normally govern purine-nucleotide biosynthesis (Brockman[13], Pardee[3]). Indirect evidence, however, suggests fast operation of the *de novo* pathway compared with "salvage" pathways (Wheeler[47,203]). Leukaemic leucocytes seem to have no defect in the interconversion of adenine and guanine[181].

One observation not shown in Fig. 11 concerns a supposed deaminase whereby 5′-AMP is converted into IMP and thence inosine, without initial dephosphorylation to give adenosine. High activity of this deaminase, as reported by D. E. Kizer and colleagues[41,118] for the Dunning and other hepatomas, is regarded by S. Fiala as an artefact, related to the high activity of adenosine deaminase already mentioned; but M. Zydowo and also Kizer's group[118] have each adduced strong evidence that liver indeed contains a 5′-AMP deaminase. Kizer[118] has argued that the rise in precancerous liver is closely linked to carcinogenesis, although one non-carcinogenic agent (α-naphthylisothiocyanate) caused a rise. However, any alterations in the capacity for AMP catabolism, whether by the deaminase pathway or by dephosphorylation[85], hardly seem to affect the supply of AMP, the level of which shows no dramatic changes in hepatocarcinogenesis.

The metabolic area shown in Fig. 11 has been little studied in connection with non-hepatic sites of neoplasia. At least for hepatocarcinogenesis it can be concluded that there is a trend towards faster catabolism of RNA and possibly of purine ribonucleotides (although the resulting purines may be catabolized more slowly), and towards faster synthesis of uridine nucleotides. Novikoff[7] has emphasized "the relative diminution of degradative pathways of purine and pyrimidine metabolism and the relative increase in their re-utilization for nucleic acid synthesis", in accordance with conclusions reached by Canellakis[73]; but it is now clear that enzymes concerned with *early* catabolic steps may be increased rather than depressed, and also that increased re-utilization (salvage) does not occur by virtue of a block in the *de novo* pathway. In general, however, the enzymic studies outlined above have been of little help in demarcating possible key steps in carcinogenesis, nor do they clinch suggestions that tumours can make use of nucleic acid precursors supplied by host tissues (cf. ref. 135).

Nucleic-acid Synthesis

In connection with the behaviour of nucleic-acid synthesis in neoplasia, facts are outweighed by assertions and speculations. thus: "the pathways to nucleic acid syntheses proceed more rapidly in malignant tissues than in non-malignant tissues generally" (Novikoff[7]); "the possibility exists that neoplastic cells have a defect in biosynthesis of the messenger-RNA necessary for biosynthesis of cytoplasmic enzymes" (Busch[14], see also Mandel[33]) The first guess is obviously likely to be true for DNA, and might well hold for most species of RNA while still being compatible with the second guess. Possibly, however, any defect in messenger RNA is not in its production but in its structure, in line with the interesting suggestion[208] that aged organisms may produce defective RNA molecules, perhaps as a result of somatic mutations.

As will become evident, there is some experimental support for the view that DNA synthesis is accelerated, and for the author's view that, at least in hepatomas, RNA is most cellular loci has faster *turnover* — the faster catabolism that is suggested by the rise in the supernatant-fraction activity of acid RNAase (see above) being offset by faster synthesis. It will also become evident that there is a need for follow-up of hints of selective changes, with neoplasia, in the rates of synthesis of different species both of DNA and of RNA. A major handicap in assessing rates of synthesis of RNA is uncertainty concerning the normal pathways for RNA synthesis, and especially the extent (conceivably appreciable) to which cytoplasmic RNA arises by synthesis directly from nucleotides rather than by movement of RNA from the nucleus (cf. ref. 212). Little is known about changes in translocation of RNA with carcinogenesis, but at least it appears that there is normal translocation of "transfer RNA" (and of attached amino acids) to microsomes in hepatomas (H. Bloemendal *et al.*[62]; C. J. Smith and E. Reid, unpublished).

There are all too few comparisons of tumours with homologous normal tissues, even by the autoradiographic technique which lends itself to such comparisons and which has been widely used in tumour studies (e.g. ref. 180). The expected high incorporation of injected thymidine into DNA has been found in hepatomas[172] and in liver after azo-dye feeding of unstated duration (A. di Marco *et al.*[31]), but not in leukaemic leucocytes[4].

In many biochemical studies there has been ill-planned choice of parameters for *in vivo* experiments (see end of Chapter 2). Inorganic phosphate is a useful precursor, if care is taken to purify the product (especially in the case of RNA); but acid-soluble inorganic phosphate as commonly measured to give a baseline may conceivably differ in specific activity from the actual nucleotide precursors, and the possibility cannot be ruled out that there might be exchange of phosphate between nucleic acids and precursors. Orotate is a useful and specific precursor for work on RNA (cf. Fig. 11), particularly since UMP is hardly concerned in terminal-nucleotide turnover in "transfer RNA". For DNA no ideal precursor is available.

DNA synthesis and RNA synthesis are best discussed together.

It should be kept in mind that the rate of DNA synthesis, which seems to be negligible in normal adult liver, is conceivably limited *in vivo* by the deoxyribonucleotide supply, and RNA synthesis by the supply of cytidine nucleotides — although hardly by ATP (see above, 5′-Ribonucleotides) as suggested by M. Revel & P. Mandel (1962[33]) and by E. Farber[91]. No assessment can yet be made of the role of "oncotrephin", isolated from hepatomas and claimed to enhance orotate incorporation into RNA in liver slices or *in vivo*[209].

Whole-animal experiments. For various reasons, for example the use of a long time interval (sometimes one day) between isotope injection and killing, most of the published comparisons of hepatomas or precancerous liver with normal liver have given somewhat inconclusive results. This remark applies to the apparent lack of a marked change in DNA or RNA synthesis in studies with precancerous liver or primary hepatomas[41,109], to the apparent rise in RNA synthesis reported from P. Mandel's laboratory in 1959[33] for an ascitic hepatoma (phosphate as precursor; cf. ref. 204), to the apparent rise in nuclear-RNA and DNA synthesis observed in a transplanted hepatoma with glycine as precursor (J. L. Irvin and collaborators[16]), and to the apparent rise in RNA and DNA synthesis observed in the Novikoff hepatoma with formate as precursor[214].

Observations reported in 1959 by H. N. Munro & C. M. Clark[41] are more conclusive: with labelled phosphate there was enhanced labelling (relative to inorganic phosphate) in the RNA of primary and transplanted liver tumours, and with labelled glycine there was enhanced labelling (relative to free glycine) in the adenine and guanine moieties of RNA.

In the author's laboratory, experiments reported in 1958[41] and 1963[163] together with unpublished experiments have established for certain hepatomas a trend towards faster RNA synthesis, judged by the incorporation of orotate in relation to the specific activity of precursor nucleotides. (G. Weber *et al.*[47a] did not examine the latter and rashly concluded that RNA synthesis was depressed). Whereas this trend seemed to be as marked with the Morris 5123 hepatoma as with rapidly growing hepatomas, a correlation between formate incorporation into nucleic acids and growth rate has been observed by G. P. Wheeler[47] and by G. Weber *et al.*[47a]; but these authors did not examine the precursor pool. The increase in RNA labelling observed by E. Reid was evident in the nuclear fraction (confirmed by M. K. Turner with purified nuclei) and in the supernatant fraction, which, with 0·25 M sucrose as the medium, may contain "rapidly labelled" RNA perhaps derived from the nucleus.

The labelling of sub-fractions prepared from purified nuclei by M. K. Turner in the author's laboratory has shown no striking change with hepatocarcinogenesis in the intra-nuclear pattern. However, an altered pattern of RNA labelling was observed in H. Busch's laboratory[53]; cf. ref. 14 & 15 with rats given thioacetamide for 9 days: at 5 minutes after intravenous injection of orotate, labelling was depressed in the nuclear fraction as a whole but enhanced in the nucleolar fraction. Moreover, a difference in the pattern of DNA labelling has been noted between an ascitic hepatoma and liver[134]; the specific activity values were respectively 15 and 5 for "nucleolar" DNA relative to "chromosomal DNA".

Liver from rats fed azo dyes for 2–5 weeks in the author's laboratory has shown no consistent change in RNA labelling (orotate as precursor), even among sub-cellular fractions as distinct from whole tissue. However, ethionine feeding gave a marked increase (not confined to any particular fraction)[196] — a rise apparently anticipating the rise in hepatomas, but surprising in view of the fall in labelling that occurs in single-dose experiments[91,144] and of the prevalent view that ethionine depresses protein synthesis. Data for cytidine nucleotides[157] seem to rule out an increase in their supply (normally rate-limiting?) as the mechanism of the increased labelling. With α-naphthylisothiocyanate, which (unlike ethionine) produced bile-duct proliferation, there was no early change in RNA labelling, although possibly an increase at 5 weeks[196].

In other *in vivo* studies (including L. Hamilton's study with adenine in leukaemic humans[181]) the precursors were compounds lying on salvage pathways. A. C. Griffin and collaborators[41] observed increased incorporation of adenine into DNA and RNA in precancerous liver and in primary hepatomas; with the latter the increase was confined to the nuclear fraction. In liver from rats fed acetylaminofluorene for 90 days and in the primary hepatoma, A. Cantarow and colleagues[41] observed notably high labelling of RNA, and also of the acid-soluble fraction, after administration of uracil; but the dose was so high that the parameter measured may well have been the capacity of the tissue to deal with an influx of uracil. With a low dose of uracil, G. Weber *et al.*[47a] found that the absolute amount incorporated into RNA was high in slow-growing hepatomas but low in fast-growing hepatomas.

Experiments with intact-cell preparations. In tissue-slice experiments with uracil at a concentration well below the saturation level for its incorporation into the RNA of liver slices, a slow-growing hepatoma (mouse) showed notably high RNA labelling[73]. Incorporation into acid-soluble nucleotides was no higher for the hepatoma than for liver, but the catabolism of uracil was decreased. The same trends were seen in regenerating liver at 60 hours after operation, although not at 48 hours[73].

Experiments *in vitro* with leucocytes were reported from R. J. Winzler's laboratory in 1958[183] and extended in 1961[181]. In chronic leukaemias, lymphatic or granulocytic, there was evidence of increased nucleic-acid labelling with the use, as precursors, of uracil, adenine, guanine, glycine, or formate — the latter likewise showing faster incorporation in acute leukaemias. With formate the main site of the nucleic-acid labelling was DNA thymine in chronic granulocytic leukaemia and RNA purines in chronic lymphatic leukaemia. With guanine it was DNA rather than RNA that showed increased labelling[181]. Assessment of nucleic-acid synthesis was not, however, the primary aim in these studies. Low incorporation of phosphate into the RNA and DNA of lymphosarcoma cells (mouse) as compared with lymphocytes (rabbit) was reported in 1954 from S. Kit's laboratory[61]. Leukaemic cells studied by F. Gavosto and A. Pileri[4] likewise seemed to have sluggish RNA synthesis. In such experiments the energy supply may have an influence: with glycine as precursor, lymphosarcoma cells surpassed thymus cells in anaerobic incorporation into nucleic acid and protein, but the converse was found aerobically[61].

Phosphate was used as precursor in tissue-slice experiments[206] in which a transplanted hepatoma gave RNA labelling no higher than that for liver; indeed, UMP isolated from the RNA showed reduced labelling relative to that of tissue inorganic phosphate. However, increased labelling of RNA nucleotides was found with formate or carbamoylaspartate as precursor, although no measurements were made on the precursor pool. Of the individual nucleotides in RNA, AMP showed a more striking increase (6-fold) in labelling than GMP with formate as precursor, and UMP showed a greater increase (2-fold) than CMP with carbamoylaspartate. Tissue-slice experiments with malignant ovarian tumours (human) showed, in comparison with benign ovarian tumours, increased uptake of phosphate into RNA and, in some experiments, into DNA[159].

So far, then, some experiments with slices as distinct from isolated cells have given results compatible with, but too equivocal to reinforce, the evidence from *in vivo* work that nucleic-acid synthesis tends to accelerate with neoplasia. It is doubtful whether physiological rates of nucleic-acid synthesis have yet been demonstrated *in vitro* with normal tissues.

Experiments with cell-free preparations. The elementary precaution of adding all four triphosphates has sometimes been neglected, as in a study[197] with isolated nuclei which, by autoradiography, showed some uptake of orotate into RNA for the Novikoff hepatoma (particularly if unlabelled RNA were added) but not for liver. The DNA-dependent "transcriptase" (Spiegelman's terminology; usually unhappily termed "RNA polymerase") — for which all four ribonucleoside triphosphates are requisite and which is believed to produce "messenger RNA" — has shown moderately reduced activity in hepatomas studied in

P. Mandel's laboratory[33], as if less "information" were needed by the hepatomas. However, for fast-growing hepatomas studied by M. K. Turner in the author's laboratory the transcriptase activity was normal or increased. In each study, results referred to DNA and results referred back to unit weight of whole tissue were similar in trend; but there remains the possibility that nuclei as isolated may not be representative of those in the tissue as a whole (see end of Chapter 2). At least it would appear that the results give little support to K. S. Kirby's suggestion[8] that together with a rise in duplicase (DNA polymerase) in tumours there is a fall in transcriptase activity. If, moreover, the rise in activity demonstrable on adding ammonium sulphate in high concentration to normal-liver transcriptase is due to increased availability of "template DNA" (by histone removal?) — as distinct from a second enzyme as suggested by C. C. Widnell (1964) — the fact that an almost normal rise is demonstrable with hepatomas indicates that the template is not grossly changed in hepatomas, despite evidence for a rise in DNA-bound histone (see beginning of Chapter).

The rise in activity claimed to occur in liver after a single injection of carcinogenic azo dye[106] may well be transient and irrelevant to carcinogenesis; no such rise was found by M. K. Turner with sustained feeding of azo dye. The same conclusion may hold for the fall in activity reported to occur after a single injection of ethionine[144]; feeding of ethionine causes, even at one week, a striking *increase* in activity, almost as marked if the experimental and control samples are each assayed in the presence of ammonium sulphate[196].

Although, as in the case of ethionine administration,[196], effects on the *in vitro* synthesis of RNA often parallel those found *in vivo*, it cannot be assumed that RNA synthesis in general is determined by the activity of transcriptase or, indeed, of any enzyme as distinct from a template or other controlling factor. Transcriptase activity could account for barely one-thousandth of the rate of RNA synthesis observed with liver *in vivo*[196]. There are reports of other enzymes (generally RNA-dependent, "replicases") for the synthesis of RNA or at least of RNA-like homopolymers, and even for the terminal addition of ribonucleotides to DNA chains; but these enzymes have yet to be studied in relation to carcinogenesis, and other enzymes await discovery.

The importance of the level of "duplicase" (DNA-dependent "DNA polymerase") in regulating DNA synthesis is uncertain, particularly since R. M. S. Smellie[16] has reported interference by an unusual nuclease. Assays in A. C. Griffin's laboratory on supernatant fractions — the activity of which is perhaps due to only one of several enzymes concerned in DNA synthesis — have shown high duplicase activity in the Novikoff hepatomas, and a striking (3-fold) but transient increase early during azo-dye feeding before cell-proliferation was evident[93].

Duplicase activity is largely retained in nuclei if organic solvents are used for their isolation (R. M. S. Smellie[16], G. Siebert[16]). Such nuclei have shown abnormally high activity in the case of the Novikoff hepatoma and especially in the case of regenerating liver (W. C. Schneider[16,16a]). In Schneider's experiments with normal-liver nuclei the possibility was recognized that the thymidine used as precursor might have been inefficiently converted into dTTP (due to lack of kinase); this possibility is not incompatible with the further observation that even whole homogenates or supernatant fractions showed low duplicase activity with normal liver as distinct from regenerating or neoplastic liver. In this careful study of an unpleasantly complex system, "native" DNA and heated DNA were compared as primers, and account was taken of the partial destruction of activity which, particularly with the hepatoma, occurred during isolation of the nuclei.

There is no information concerning solid hepatomas of the minimum-deviation type. There are, however, reports by Bianchi[60,4] of high incorporation of dTMP into DNA by cell-free preparations from a lymphosarcoma as compared with lymph nodes, and also by preparations from leukaemia leucocytes (acute or myeloid leukaemia) for which, however, no normal-leucocyte baseline was provided.

CHAPTER 8

Control Mechanisms

THERE is accumulating evidence that some derangement in "control mechanisms" governing enzymic activities underlies the neoplastic transformation, or is at least closely linked to the transformation. Before this field is surveyed, a brief recapitulation will be made of some trends already mentioned (Chapter 4–7) for the biochemistry of tumours, or at least of hepatomas. As has been indicated above in various contexts, trends in primary tumours are often foreshadowed in precancerous tissues, although probably only a few cells become cancerous; in a few respects, however, precancerous liver has shown at some stage a biochemical change converse to that appearing in the hepatoma[41].

Metabolic Parameters in Relation to Tumour Development

Although hepatomas having fewer "deviations" from liver than the Morris 5123 are now available[35,40], deviations common to this slow-growing hepatoma and to rapidly growing hepatomas warrant collation. The salient deviations as listed in 1962[37] are (1) faulty drug metabolism, (2) no acetoacetate shunt (shuttle), (3) no tryptophan pyrrolase induction [see below], (4) poor glycogen storage, (5) no bile production [although certain hepatomas *can* produce bile]. Apart from (2), these deviations concern the cytomembranes (endoplasmic reticulum)[37], and accord with electron-microscopic changes (Chapter 1) and with the poor yield of microsomal protein and RNA that is evident not only with hepatomas but also with precancerous liver[41,163] (the undiminished yield during ethionine feeding being an exception). Particular emphasis has been placed on changes in the lipoprotein membranes, and on possible implications not only for processes such as cholesterol synthesis but also for genetic expression (A. A. Hadjiolov[21]); but ribosomes or polysomes may also be affected (cf. ref. 200).

The possibility that the mitochondrial membrane is "below par" in hepatomas[37] — cf. (2) above — is supported by observations on mitochondrial yield and nucleotide content[41,163]. For the nucleus there is little evidence on which to base an opinion. At least the evidence for cytoplasmic derangements is strong.

Changes in respiratory capacity and in other parameters of energy metabolism, as summarized by Weber[202] for hepatomas (Table 4; cf. Fig. 8, Chapter 5), may in some instances be important as late steps in the process of tumour progression represented in Fig. 1, Chapter 1, but are unlikely to be crucial to the neoplastic transformation (see also Aisenberg[6], Emmelot[41]). Attention to the neglected topic of lipids (including phospholipids) may disclose an important derangement in this metabolic area. The picture for protein and amino acid metabolism (Chapter 6) is not as clear as the *in vitro* results in Table 4 would suggest. No importance can yet be attached to changes in respect of catalase, of —SH groups or of NAD; but there are decreases, conceivably important, in NADP and especially in $NADH_2$ and $NADPH_2$ — hardly in accord with the supposed "reductive environment" in cancer cells.

Amongst acid-soluble 5′-ribonucleotides[163], UDPglucuronate and purine nucleotides show in at least some hepatomas a depletion which, although hardly important in itself, might be the outcome of some more fundamental derangement. At least it is unlikely that there is a crucial reduction in nucleotide catabolism, or in uridine nucleotide synthesis. Indeed, both of the pathways for the latter may have an increased capacity in fast-growing tumours, and there may be diversion of carbamoyl phosphate from urea synthesis into the *de novo* route to UMP. There is evidence of faster turnover of RNA, not yet proved to be a "minimum deviation". The few results so far available for the

TABLE 4. CORRELATION OF METABOLIC FACTORS WITH GROWTH RATE IN TRANSPLANTED HEPATOMAS

Essentially as tabulated (with literature citations) by G. Weber *et al.*[47,47a,201] The results are grouped from the point of view of definite trends which fit into one of three categories, and usually (although not for amino-acid incorporation) are on a cell basis rather than a wet-weight basis. The direction of the trend for a parameter is indicated by an arrow showing whether it increased (↑) or decreased (↓) with the increasing growth rate.

Correlation with growth rate	Low or high in all hepatomas	No correlation with growth rate
↓ Glucose-6-phosphatase	↑ Glucose-6-phosphate dehydrogenase	Cellularity
↓ Fructose diphosphatase	↓ Glycogen	Lactate dehydrogenase
↓ Phosphoenolpyruvate carboxykinase	↓ Phosphoglucomutase	Phosphohexose isomerase
↓ Pyruvate carboxylase	↓ Fructose uptake	6-Phosphogluconate dehydrogenase
↓ Malate dehydrogenase	↓ Fructose to CO_2	Activation of phosphoglucomutase
↓ Pyruvate to glucose	↓ Nitrogen content	Malic enzyme
↑ Lactate production	↓ Glucose to fatty acid	Aldolase
↑ C-1/C-6 oxidation of glucose	↓ Orotate incorporation into RNA *in vivo**	Oxidation of amino acids (alanine, aspartate, glycine, serine, isoleucine, valine)
↑ K_m of phosphoglucomutase	Responsiveness to adrenocorticoid†:	
↑ Incorporation of amino acids into protein (alanine, aspartate, glycine, serine, isoleucine, valine)	↓ —amino-acid level	Amino-acid level
↑ Fructose into glycogen through hexokinase reaction	↓ —RNA level	RNA level
↓ Fructose into glycogen through fructokinase reaction		
↑ Formate incorporation into RNA *in vivo**		
Responsiveness to adrenocorticoid†:		
↓ —enzymes of gluconeogenesis		
↓ —glycogenesis		
↓ —uracil incorporation into RNA		

* See Chapter 7; the 'precusor pool' was not examined.
† See Chapter 8, Table 6 and 7.

supply of 5′-deoxyribonucleotides and for DNA synthesis leave open the attractive possibility that a crucial change will be found within this area. The apparent rise in DNA-bound histone (O. Frankfurt[31]) seemed not to be crucial, being demonstrable (histochemically) only in truly malignant tumours, but it illustrates an approach that needs exploitation (cf. ref. 103).

In connection with speculations about metabolic changes linked with tumour progression as distinct from the actual neoplastic transformation, there is little information for any single primary tumour studied through its life-span (but see Cowdry[7], and Metastases, Chapter 4). Most of the relevant data are derived from comparisons, necessarily less satisfactory, amongst different generations of a transplanted tumour, or amongst different transplanted tumours supposedly similar in cell origin, but caused by different agents. There are now several examples of changes apparently associated with transplantation itself, perhaps irrelevant to the phenomenon of progression. Chromosomal changes (Chapter 1; Koller[7,21]) will not be discussed here.

Changes with transplantation. The dCMP aminohydrolase activity of a hepatoma studied in P. Emmelot's laboratory[32,*105*] rose sharply at about the 10th generation. H. C. Pitot and collaborators reported in 1961[35] a difference between sub-lines of the Morris 5123 hepatoma in the influence of sex on threonine dehydrase activity. Certain enzymes such as glucose-6-phosphatase showed a tendency towards lower activity in the 1st or 2nd generation transplants of a hepatoma compared with the primary (ethionine-induced) hepatoma[37]; as was argued in Chapter 2, it is unlikely that admixture of normal cells in the primary tumour could account for such results, and indeed a hepatoma studied in the author's laboratory has shown a rise in glucose-6-phosphatase from one transplant generation to the next. Different sub-lines of a Morris hepatoma have shown a difference in growth rate[200], and a notable difference in catalase activity, which was close to normal in a fast-growing sub-line[88,158].

Hepatomas transferred to tissue culture appear to lose tryptophan pyrrolase, glucose-6-phosphate dehydrogenase and proline oxidase (H. C. Pitot *et al.*[38,43]; cf. G. H. Sato and V. Buonassisi[43]). The finding of antigenic simplification on converting a solid tumour to an ascitic form[30] reinforces the warning expressed in Chapter 2 concerning the use of ascitic tumours as test material. The ascitic conversion entailed a dramatic and irreversible fall in 5′-nucleotidase in the case of a squamous-cell carcinoma[193] (although there is the complication that 5′-nucleotidase is in part associated with blood-vessel walls), and a fall in cytoplasmic particles (per unit DNA) in the case of a sarcoma studied by E. Klein in 1955[30].

Enzymic Aspects of Molecular Biology in Relation to Cancer

A convenient starting-point for closer discussion of cancer from the viewpoint of control mechanisms (especially for those concerned in cell division) is the 'deletion theory' as outlined in Chapter 2. This theory is still alive and vigorous, having been given a "new look" by V. R. Potter[8,40] and his colleagues[39] in the light of growing knowledge in the field of molecular biology. It must be emphasized that this knowledge, as summarized in Fig. 12 (see also Fig. 14, later in Chapter) rests on experiments with micro-organisms, which conceivably differ from higher organisms in quantitative respects such as the life-span of "messenger RNA" (the half-life in a mammalian experiment by Pitot[47] being apparently many hours) and the role of repression and de-repression as distinct from other control mechanisms (A. B. Pardee[3]), and may even differ in the actual nature of hereditary mechanisms (as suggested by I. Leslie[1]).

Revised deletion-hypothesis. Early forms of the deletion hypothesis emphasized loss of a particular enzyme or enzymes (catabolic ?) concerned in some way with growth regulation — perhaps entailing imbalance between metabolic pathways competing for a key intermediate. The Millers' observation[37] of protein deletion in azo-dye hepatomas accorded well with the idea of enzyme deletion.

The recent observation[37] that the protein in question is *not* lacking in the Morris 5123 hepatoma has been a stimulus to re-phrasing of the hypothesis (Potter[8]). The essence of the revised deletion

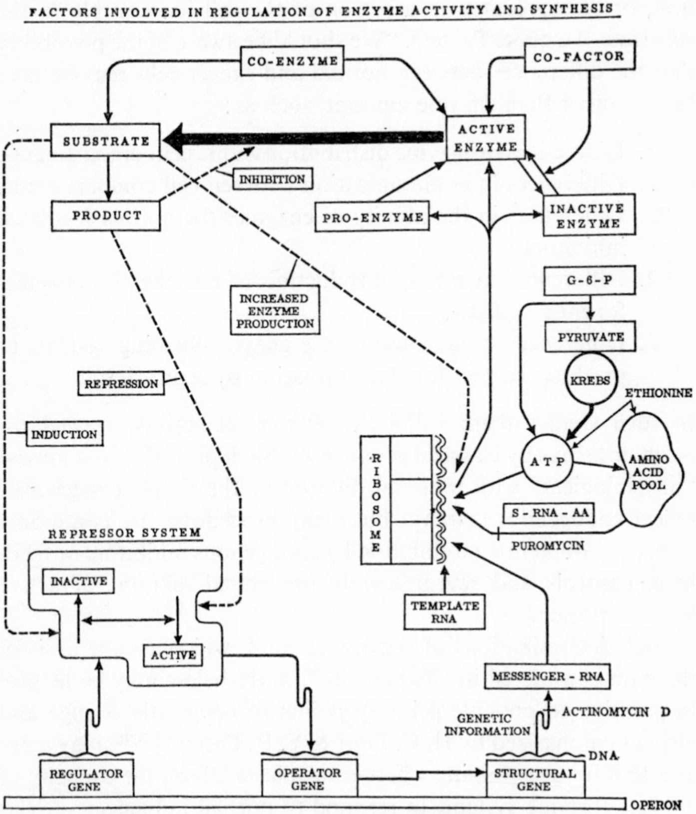

FIG. 12. Concepts in molecular biology (G. Weber[46]).

hypothesis is that neoplasia is attributable to loss of a repression mechanism which, in normal tissues, restrains DNA synthesis ("feedback deletion").

Since repressors are themselves produced by enzymes, such de-repression may well arise from loss of an enzyme activity in the affected cell — although not necessarily loss of enzyme protein or even of activity as assayed *in vitro*. The enzyme protein may, for example, be in an inactive configuration due to allosteric inhibition, or be segregated in a region of the cell inaccessible to the substrate. To quote Potter[8], "We should be aware of the possibility that the differences between normal and cancer cells may involve factors other than enzyme amount, such as:

"1. Differences in enzyme distribution within cell compartments.
"2. Differences in communication between cell compartments.
"3. Differences in the affinity of enzymes for normal feedback inhibitors.
"4. Differences in rate of production of enzymes by enzyme-forming systems.
"5. Differences in response of the enzyme-forming systems to products responsible for regulation by repression."

In such studies there still is, as Potter recognizes, a need for enzymic assays by classical procedures. Such procedures, if almost "physiological" with minimal dilution of the tissue, conceivably reflect endogenous activity; but assay procedures are commonly such as to obliterate modulation by endogenous inhibitors or feedback controls and reveal merely the actual amount of active enzyme protein.

Such determinations of enzyme amount, which are the basis of the data considered in Chapters 4–7, nevertheless may be helpful in pointing to possible primary points of neoplastic change and also, as emphasized by H. C. Pitot & V. R. Potter[8,37,40], may serve as a tool for ascertaining whether neoplasia affects the capacity of enzyme-forming systems to respond to normal influences such as diet or hormones. The latter topic is dealt with later. The question of compartmentation will first be touched on.

Intracellular compartmentation. It has long been obvious that the cell is far from being a mere bag of enzymes, substrates and cofactors. There are many examples of segregation of enzymes, for example of succinate dehydrogenase within mitochondria. If a substrate or cofactor were actually separated by a membrane from the enzyme in question, enzyme action would necessitate congregation of the reaction components — except perhaps for enzymes actually situated within the membrane structure, or for reaction chains incorporating a "bypass" such as the "shuttle" systems mentioned in Chapter 5. Much has yet to be learnt about compartmentation and especially about control mechanisms depending on changes in compartmentation. Moreover, as remarked by Novikoff[7] in the context of some fragmentary observations concerning lactate dehydrogenase and $NADH_2$-cytochrome *c* reductase, "Considerably less is known concerning "compartmentation" in cancer cells than in liver cells."

Mention has already been made of compartmentation of ATP and other acid-soluble nucleotides within mitochondria (perhaps with a damaged barrier in tumour cells; Chapter 5) and possibly within the nucleus (Chapter 7). Although the nucleus is notably rich in Na^+ ions, it is uncertain whether the nuclear membrane restricts the passage into the cytoplasm of constituents such as messenger-RNA or ribosomes, and whether there is a true nuclear compartment for glycolytic and other soluble enzymes which definitely exist within the nucleus although also present in the cytoplasm (G. Siebert[16]; A. Claude[21]). The enzyme system concerned in the formation of NAD, or rather of deamido-NAD, is unusual in being apparently confined to the nucleus, possibly linked to nuclear structures (chromatin? or ribosomes[195]?); the binding appears to be tighter than for duplicase (DNA polymerase)[16]. The possibility that, within the nucleus itself, there may be segregation of enzymes in the nucleolus (cf. ref. 15) has been little explored.

The appearance of lysosomal enzymes in supernatant fractions, as instanced by acid RNAase in hepatomas (Chapter 7), may connote a metabolically important juxtaposition of enzyme and substrate — perhaps really an enzyme shift from lysosomes to specialized vacuoles (Fig. 2, Chapter 1) which are sites of catabolism and which readily disintegrate *in vitro* with liberation of their contents. Such juxtaposition is emphasized in a recent theory of carcinogenesis[55]. For the cytomembranes there is no conclusive evidence of inaccessibility of substrates to enzymes, although there are unexplained findings such as a rise in glucose-6-phosphatase activity on adding deoxycholate *in vitro*. With hepatocarcinogenesis, microsomes show interesting changes in their capacity to "swell" *in vitro* (J. Arcos[37,41]); but interpretation is difficult, particularly since the cytomembrane system undergoes structural rearrangement during homogenization.

In general, there are too few facts to allow of profitable speculation about altered compartmentation in cancer cells. Such alterations, if present *in vivo*, could explain certain reported changes in the distribution of enzymes amongst sub-cellular fractions. However, few of the many such studies (e.g. refs. 41, 138, 169, 191, 205) have got to grips with interpretation, affected as this is by methodological artefacts and enzyme plurality. Where an enzyme is associated with more than one kind of morphological element, it does not follow that there is a single protein with a single function, common to each locus.

Properties of enzyme proteins. In support of the possibility that carcinogens may themselves exert allosteric effects, Emmelot[21] has shown that, *in vitro*, the hepatocarcinogen 4-(4′-dimethylaminophenyl)azoquinoline can, like thyroxine and stilboestrol, inhibit glutamate dehydrogenase with formation of sub-units possessing alanine dehydrogenase activity. Concerning another possibility (Potter[8]), that with neoplasia there may be changes in enzyme properties such as affinity for feedback inhibitors, the scanty evidence is summarized in Table 5. All that can be said is that there are some hints of alterations in properties, but that for purified as distinct from crude enzyme preparations there is a notable lack of information. There is a particular need for attention to enzymes concerned in metabolic processes that might be determinants or concomitants of cell division. Much information is now available on apparent feed-back control of enzymes concerned in purine nucleotide synthesis[13], in dTMP synthesis from thymidine (inhibited by dTTP; Potter[16]), and in other processes (Bresnick[47], Pardee[3], Umbarger[21]; see also refs. 16a, 43) — although effects demonstrable *in vitro* with some supposed feedback inhibitors entail concentrations well above the endogenous levels.

Enzyme-forming systems. V. R. Potter and his colleagues have now oriented their work on tumours towards "metabolic adaptations", in the sense of a change in enzyme activity following changes in dietary or endocrine balance. Here it may be pointed out that "enzyme induction" in such situations represents an acceleration, rather than a switching-on, of enzyme synthesis; in common with most other cell constituents, enzymes are not "static" but are subject to "turnover", and the enzyme levels as discussed in preceding chapters really reflect a balance between synthesis and breakdown of enzyme protein.

Massive dosage with cortisone is a useful tool for achieving "induction" of certain enzymes, although it should not be assumed that induction thus obtained reflects a physiological as distinct from pharmacological process; such treatment might conceivably act by suppressing the endogenous output of a different adrenocorticoid.

The few examples of inducible (adaptive) enzymes so far established for mammals are, unfortunately, hardly likely to be key enzymes in cell growth — unless it is argued, in the context of certain enzymes that show high activity with liver regeneration, that partial hepatectomy is an inducing stimulus. Moreover, it has not been proved in every case of "adaptation" that with increased activity there is a true increase in the amount of enzyme protein. Often, when the responsiveness of normal and tumour tissues has been compared, there has been a further but self-imposed handicap that the tumours studied had been repeatedly transplanted — which may well have led to loss of dependence on hormonal or other controlling influences (cf. ref. 30, and earlier in this Chapter).

Turning now to neoplasia, no attempt will be made to consider effects of injected ethionine — which blocks the induction of

TABLE 5. PROPERTIES OF INDIVIDUAL ENZYMES IN TUMOURS AND HOMOLOGOUS NORMAL TISSUES

(In Tables 5–7 the topics are listed in an order similar to that used earlier in the book.)

Tumour (and normal tissue, if not evident)	Enzyme	Properties studied, and *tumour abnormality* (if any)	Reference
Hepatoma or squamous-cell carcinoma	Acid phosphates (3 different enzymes?)	Ratio of components, and chromatographic and enzymic properties, e.g. specificity: only *ratio altered*	139
Hepatomas, including minimum deviation	Aldolase	Activity towards fructose-1-phosphate (compared with -1,6-diphosphate) — *high* (as in embryonic tissues)	178
Jensen sarcoma (muscle)	Lactate dehydrogenase, purified	Catalytic and immunological properties	F. Kubowitz & P. Ott, 1943[25]
Epidermal carcinoma, primary	Lactate dehydrogenase	pH optimum, K_m	125
Myeloid-leukaemia leucocytes	Lactate dehydrogenase	Chromatographic and electrophoretic components — *ratios altered*	P. Dioguardi & A. Agostoni[4]
Thyroid (*inter alia*) and colonic tumours, human (adjoining uninvolved tissue)	Lactate dehydrogenase	Iso-enzymes — *increased ratio of* M (*muscle*) *form to H* (*heart*) *form*	97a

Hepatomas, including minimum deviation	Phosphoglucomutase	K_m; activation by pre-incubation procedure — *higher* K_m *if hepatoma fast-growing*	G. Weber *et. al.*[47]
Hepatomas, not minimum deviation	Histidine decarboxylase, crude	pH optimum, activation by organic solvents — *altered* to foetal-liver behaviour	[115]
Hepatomas, minimum deviation	Pyrroline 5-carboxylate reductase	Feedback inhibition by proline	H. C. Pitot[3]
Hepatomas, not minimum deviation	Acid DNAase, acid and alkaline RNAases, crude or semi-pure	pH optima	M. E. Maver & A. E. Greco, 1956[136]
Hepatomas, Novikoff & Morris 3683	Acid RNAase, purified (purer from hepatoma ?)	Loss of — SH and of activity after *p*-chloromercuribenzoate — *activity lost more readily*	[136]
Hepatomas, including minimum deviation	Thymidine phosphorylase (dual-function enzyme ?)	Capacity to transfer deoxyribose moiety to 2nd molecule of base: *lacking* (but normal capacity in many human tumours)	[216]
Hepatoma, not minimum deviation	dCMP aminohydrolase, crude	pH optimum, K_m, inhibition by high substrate concentration	G. C. Hartman & E. Reid (cf.[105])
Hepatomas, minimum deviation	Thymidine kinase	Feedback inhibition by dTTP	D. H. Ives *et al.*, see Pitot[3]

TABLE 5 *continued*

Tumour (and normal tissue, if not evident)	Enzyme	Properties studied, and *tumour abnormality* (if any)	Reference
Hepatomas, various	Thymidine kinase(s), semi-pure	Feedback inhibition by dCTP — *abolished* in fast-growing hepatomas (or regenerating liver)	66
Leukaemic leucocytes, chronic myelogenous or lymphatic	Thymidine kinase	Feedback inhibition by dCTP, dTTP, etc.	E. Bresnick & R. J. Karjala[66]
Hepatomas, e.g. 5123, H-35, ascitic Novikoff	Aspartate trans-carbamoylase, purified	pH optimum, K_m, V_{max}, response to feedback or other inhibitors	66
Hepatomas, primary or precancerous liver	Guanase, crude	pH curve: *sharpened*, with no change in optimum	T. Takahashi, 1954[41]
Precancerous liver, azo-dye	Xanthine oxidase, crude	Time course: *earlier falling off* (enzyme loss?)	K. Okuda, 1959[41]

various enzymes[91] (cf. Fig. 12) but which is not carcinogenic in single doses. From the results summarized in Table 6 and in Fig. 13, it is evident that certain adaptations are impaired in many hepatomas and even in precancerous liver, but that most of the examples shown are unlikely to be minimum deviations. However, "The few instances of a pure substrate induction of tryptophan

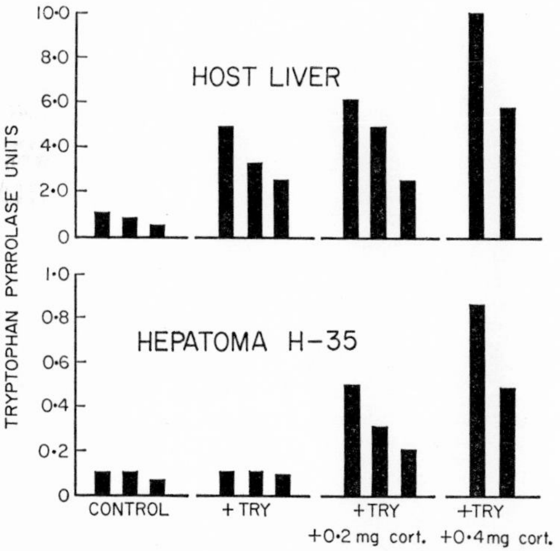

FIG. 13. The "permissive" effect of cortisone on tryptophan pyrrolase induction in host liver and Reuber hepatoma H-35 (H. C. Pitot[46]). *All* rats were adrenalectomized. +TRY denotes administration of tryptophan. The daily dose of cortisone is indicated on the axis, except for the "controls" (viz. hepatoma-bearing rats given no tryptophan) which received 0·2 mg per day.

pyrrolase in highly differentiated [minimum deviation] hepatomas appear to be of the "permissive" type rather than "pure", requiring interaction of both hormone and substrate" (Pitot[46]). "Permissive" in this context means that a dose of hormone which itself has no effect enables the substrate to produce its effect (see Fig. 13).

Pitot[38,46] speculated that in hepatomas the RNA template for

TABLE 6. RESPONSIVENESS OF TUMOUR ENZYMIC ACTIVITIES TO FACTORS WHICH AFFECT THE CORRESPONDING NORMAL TISSUE

Tumour (and normal tissue, if not evident)	Activity	Factor and normal effect, and *tumour behaviour*	Reference
Hepatomas, Morris 5123	Catalase	Protein deprivation: fall — *unresponsive*	M. J. Rechcigl *et al.* 1961[35]
Hepatomas, various	Azo-dye *N*-demethylase	Methylcholanthrene: rise — *primary hepatoma unresponsive* (5123 responsive)	A. H. Conney & J. J. Burns[46]
Hepatomas, various	Glucose-6-phosphate dehydrogenase	Cortisone *in vivo*, or diet — e.g. re-feeding after fast: rise — *unresponsive*, except that 5123 responds to diet	H. C. Pitot & V. R. Potter[46]
Precancerous liver, azo-dye	Glucose-6-phosphatase	Cortisone *in vivo*: rise — *less responsive*	S. Fiala & A. Fiala, 1959[41]
Hepatomas or precancerous liver	Glucose-6-phosphatase	Thyroxine injection: rise — *responsive* (even some ethionine — but not azo-dye — hepatomas)	A. B. El-Aaser & E. Reid, unpubld.
Hepatomas, various	Glucose-6-phosphatase, fructose diphosphatase	Triamcinolone (adrenocorticoid) *in vivo*: rise — *unresponsive*, except that slow-growing hepatomas give slight response	G. Weber *et al.*[47a]
Hepatomas, various (sometimes host liver!)	Tryptophan pyrrolase	Substrate or cortisone *in vivo*: rise which, for substrate effect in adren-	H. C. Pitot[37,46]; see also [35,76,88]

		alectomized rats, needs "permissive" amount of corticoid — *unresponsive*, except that *certain hepatomas* (not 5123) *respond to substrate if adrenal cortex intact, and feebly respond to cortisone*	
Precancerous liver, azo-dye	Tryptophan pyrrolase	Substrate *in vivo*: rise — *less responsive* even at 10 days	S. Fiala & A. Fiala, 1959[41]; cf. N. D. Lee & R. H. Williams, 1952
Hepatomas, various	Threonine (or serine) dehydrase	Substrate or cortisone *in vivo*: rise — *unresponsive*, except that *certain hepatomas sometimes respond*	H. C. Pitot[35,46]
		Glucose *in vivo*: repression — *unresponsive*	H. C. Pitot *et al.*, 1964[38]
Hepatomas, various (sometimes host liver!)	Tyrosine-oxoglutarate transaminase	Substrate or cortisone *in vivo*: rise — *hyper-responsiveness sometimes found*, e.g. for 5123 in adrenalectomized rats	H. C. Pitot[35,46]
Precancerous liver, azo-dye	Acid DNAase	Liver regeneration: rise — *hyper-responsive* or, with longer feeding, *less responsive*	S. Brody, 1960[41]
Hepatoma, Morris 5123	Pyrimidine reductase	Diet, e.g. high protein level: rise — *unresponsive*	T. Ono *et al.*, 1963[40]

synthesis of tryptophan pyrrolase is abnormally unstable but can be maintained or renewed under adrenocorticoid influence. Neither this suggestion, not his suggestion[37] that there is impairment of the final stage of enzyme synthesis whereby the completed protein is released from the endoplasmic reticulum, entails any alteration in the nuclear output of messenger RNA — an aspect which is considered below, together with later work on template stability. Evidence is in fact accumulating (cf, ref. 91) that in normal cells there are important cytoplasmic (ribosomal?) loci at which agents controlling protein synthesis may operate. Such evidence renders plausible a theory of carcinogenesis[39] to be mentioned later.

Various metabolic "adaptations". Even before the recent interest in enzyme adaptation, information was accumulating concerning changes, with neoplasia, in the adaptivity of metabolic processes for which the key enzyme was not assayed or even delineated. These studies, as listed in Table 7, confirm that tumours and precancerous tissue are commonly unresponsive to influences such as hormones (although it is dubious whether the effects with hormones *in vitro* are "physiological"). The processes to which this conclusion refers include mitosis, respiration, and the synthesis (perhaps determined by energy supply) of protein and nucleic acids. From the few studies of facets of glucose utilization — the formation of acid-soluble organic phosphate observed in the presence of glucose by Kit perhaps being one facet — it appears that unresponsiveness may here be found only to influences which are normally inhibitory.

It would evidently be premature to make generalizations about tumours, particularly since the approaches indicated in Table 7 await thorough application to minimum-deviation hepatomas. Eventually, however, the search for impairments of "metabolic adaptations" — random though they appear to be in character (Potter[21]) — should help in the delineation of inevitable and important consequences of the neoplastic transformation, even if it may not readily give a direct lead to the primary step or steps.

Consideration will now be given to nucleic acids, these presumably being directly or at least indirectly concerned in the primary changes underlying neoplasia.

Genetic Aspects of Molecular Biology in Relation to Cancer

No new theories will be developed here, nor can justice be done to Potter's masterly presentation[40] of a "reconciling assumption" to bridge the apparent gap between the viral and the somatic-mutation theories outlined in Chapter 2. He argues that viral nucleic acid could in fact cause a "somatic mutation" through a transformation or transduction mechanism; possibly "both RNA and DNA tumour-producing viruses may become integrated into the genome of normal cells in order to convert them to tumour cells". Emmelot[21] has made similar suggestions, and with respect to the alternative idea that there could be a change "affecting the expression of the genetic information" he remarks: "This represents de-differentiation, in the sense of an "acquired" loss to respond to the growth control mechanism as a result of a change in the metabolic state of the cell".

Immunological theories will not be considered, there being at present no imaginable mechanism whereby immune processes, for example at the cell surface, could influence genetic processes. E. Borek's argument (see Magee[19]) that changes in the enzymic methylation of RNA are crucial to carcinogenesis will not be discussed, on the grounds that so far there have been no comparisons of tumours with homologous normal tissues in respect of this theory — or indeed of certain other theories.

The reader is recommended to refresh his memory by glancing again at Chapters 3, 6 and 7, particularly the late parts of these Chapters, which may provide a framework for the ideas now to be discussed. For general orientation, Fig. 14 may be consulted in conjunction with Fig. 12.

Might the neoplastic transformation centre on RNA? Some carcinogens or mutagens — these terms often being regarded as

TABLE 7. RESPONSIVENESS OF TUMOUR METABOLISM (*in vivo*, OR INTACT CELLS *in vitro*) TO FACTORS WHICH AFFECT THE CORRESPONDING NORMAL TISSUE

Tumour (and normal tissue, if not evident)	Metabolic process or other parameter	Factor and normal effect, and *tumour behaviour*	Reference
Hepatomas, primary, or precancerous liver	Mitosis *in vivo*	Partial hepatectomy: mitosis in remaining liver — *unresponsive*; but adenomatous foci in late-precancerous liver may respond	M. M. Maini & H. F. Stich, 1962[1]; Gel'shtein[95]; cf. S. Brody[41] and J. M. Vasiliev[55]
Early precancerous epidermis, dimethylbenzanthracene	Mitosis *in vivo*	Cortisone *in vivo*: suppression (block in carbohydrate utilization?) — *unresponsive*	100
Primary sarcoma explants (fibroblasts), or hepatoma explants	Mitosis *in vitro*	Carcinogenic hydrocarbons (fibroblasts) or *o*-aminoazotoluene (liver): suppression — *unresponsive*	J. M. Vasiliev (cf. A. Haddow)[55]
Lymphosarcoma (thymus, etc.)	Aerobic utilization of glucose	Adrenocortical extract or ACTH *in vivo*: normally no effect — *enhanced utilization* (but no rise in lactate accumulation)	166
Precancerous liver, 9 months	Respiration and aerobic glycolysis, slices	Thyroxine *in vitro* in presence of CoA: stimulation — *unresponsive with respect to respiration*	E. Le Breton & Y. Moulé[12]
Leukaemic leucocytes	Glycogenesis from glucose, aerobic	Insulin *in vitro*: stimulation—*responsive*	127
Hepatomas, including minimum deviation	Cholesterol synthesis	Dietary cholesterol: inhibition of synthesis — *unresponsive*	M. D. Siperstein[47]

Hepatomas, not minimum deviation	Protein and RNA content; glycine or phosphate incorporation into RNA *in vivo*	Protein deprivation: fall in RNA and protein, rise in incorporation — *unresponsive*	H. N. Munro & C. M. Clark, 1959[41]
Lymphosarcoma, mouse (lymphatic cells, rabbit)	Incorporation of amino acid into protein and of phosphate into acid-soluble organic phosphate (intact cells, aerobic)	Corticoids *in vitro*: suppression of incorporation — *less responsive* (amino acid) or *hyper-responsive* (phosphate)	S. Kit *et al.*, 1953, 1954[61]
Lymphosarcoma (thymus)	Glycine incorporation into protein and nucleic acid (intact cells, aerobic or anaerobic)	Steroids, e.g. hydrocortisone, *in vitro*: inhibition of incorporation and of respiration or anaerobic glycolysis — *unresponsive* only in respect of anaerobic glycolysis inhibition	61
Hepatomas	Valine incorporation into protein (slices)	Anaerobiosis: inhibition of incorporation — *responsive* (i.e. usual inhibition)	A. C. Aisenberg (see Potter[21,46])
Hepatomas, minimum deviation	Polysome pattern	Brief fasting: alteration in pattern — *unresponsive* (i.e. no alteration)	200
Hepatomas (transplanted) or precancerous liver	Orotate incorporation into RNA *in vivo*, relative to tissue precursor	Thyroxine injection: stimulation — hepatomas *often unresponsive*	E. Reid (unpublished)
Hepatomas, various	Orotate or uracil incorporation into RNA *in vivo*; amino-acid level	Triamcinolone (adrenocorticoid) *in vivo*: fall (orotate) or rise (uracil; amino acids) — *unresponsive*, except that slow-growing hepatomas show rise with uracil	G. Weber *et al.*[47a]

virtually synonymous — can undoubtedly bind to RNA or alter its structure (Chapter 3), as can some anti-cancer agents to be mentioned in Chapter 9. Such studies have all too often dealt with whole-tissue RNA rather than with RNA in particular loci. At

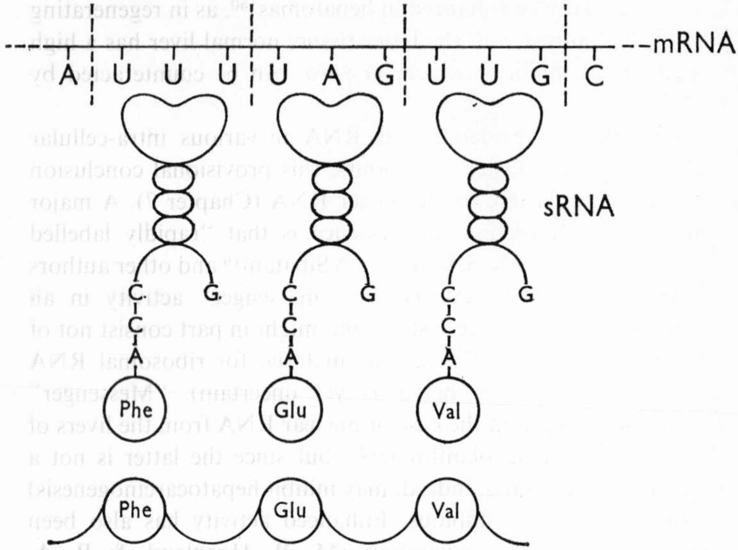

FIG. 14. Guiding role of messenger RNA (mRNA) in protein synthesis (from ref. [18a]). The mRNA is attached to ribosomes (which themselves contain RNA, the role of which is obscure). Molecules of transfer RNA (soluble RNA, sRNA) each carrying its appropriate amino acid attached to the terminal nucleotide sequence, C–C–A, align themselves in appropriate order along a strand of messenger RNA. The amino acids link together forming a polypeptide chain, which then peels off. For the different amino acids, different species of sRNA are required.

least it seems unlikely that there will prove to be a crucial defect in "transfer RNA" (or, as it is sometimes loosely termed, "soluble RNA"), affecting the rate of amino-acid activation or actual code recognition. It is conceivable that, in line with observations mentioned early in this chapter, there is a defect in the cytomembranes (endoplasmic reticulum), perhaps particularly in ribosomal RNA itself or in the linkage of ribosomes to form polysomes[200] (cf. ref. 91). There is some evidence that the responsiveness of ribosomes to messenger RNA as judged by amino-acid incorporation may actually be enhanced in hepatomas[150], as in regenerating liver[107]. In contrast with the latter tissue, normal liver has a high content of an inhibitor which, *in vitro*, can be counteracted by GTP[107].

Whilst there is evidence that RNA in various intra-cellular loci is synthesized faster in tumours, this provisional conclusion may not be applicable to messenger RNA (Chapter 7). A major difficulty in interpreting the evidence is that "rapidly labelled RNA" as studied by K. S. Kirby[116], A Sibatani[16] and other authors has not always been assayed for "messenger" activity in an amino-acid incorporating system, and might in part consist not of messenger RNA but of precursor material for ribosomal RNA (the role of the latter being as yet uncertain). "Messenger" activity is enhanced in the case of nuclear RNA from the livers of rats given 3-methylcholanthrene[126], but since the latter is not a hepatocarcinogen (and, indeed, may inhibit hepatocarcinogenesis) the interpretation is dubious. Enhanced activity has also been found during liver regeneration (M. B. Hoagland & B. A. Askonas, 1963[107]).

Possible complications in the study of messenger RNA are that defects in RNA primary structure and hence in coding are conceivable (cf. ref. 208, and quotation below from Emmelot[21]), that defects in secondary structure could arise (perhaps *in vitro*) and reduce the capacity to form polysomes, and that any fall in the output of RNA species governing the synthesis of non-essential cytoplasmic proteins might well be accompanied by, and masked by, an increased output of the RNA that codes for proteins essential for cell division. In connection with the possibility that the supply of messenger RNA is determined, in tumours, by its breakdown rather than its production, useful information might be gained by closer study of RNAases with attention to supposed ribosomal and nuclear RNAases (cf. I. Leslie[1]) and with trial, as substrates, of

RNA fractions from the same tissue — ideally including messenger-RNA fractions.

Indirectly, from observations on the induction of tryptophan pyrrolase (see above), Pitot was led to the concept that the "template" is abnormally unstable in hepatomas, particularly after adrenalectomy (the enhanced instability after adrenalectomy being, in Potter's view[21], a particularly notable observation). For a series of inducible enzymes studied with actinomycin D as a tool, Pitot[38] obtained evidence of a general tendency, in hepatomas towards low stability of template systems (conceivably of the membrane component). Thus, when threonine dehydrase was induced in liver by administration of casein hydrolysate to protein-deprived rats, the initiation of enzyme synthesis (presumably through build-up of messenger RNA) was not curtailed if actinomycin D was injected at the onset of initiation; on the other hand, with hepatomas the small but steady rise in enzyme occurring, with little time lag, after the casein hydrolysate was markedly depressed by actinomycin D, as if constant replenishment of messenger RNA were necessary for continued synthesis in hepatomas. However, for thymidine kinase as studied in V. R. Potter's laboratory, the converse was found: it appeared that the template was *more* stable in hepatomas.

From such observations, Pitot[38] suggested that "alterations in template stability at the molecular level can at the cellular, tissue and organism level lead in one way or another to the thousands of biochemical, pathological and clinical syndromes we associate with the disease cancer". On similar lines, Emmelot[21] has speculated: "And what would be the result if stable messenger-RNA templates with growth control information, which would be replenished only slowly, if at all, by suppressed structural genes (such templates would behave more or less as the hypothetical plasmagens), were to be destroyed or made non-sensical?" It is obviously important that the central objective — to learn how growth is controlled — should not be lost sight of in future work on enzyme induction and template stability.

Might the neoplastic transformation centre on DNA? The view is still prevalent that cancer cells are irreversibly dedifferentiated. However, evidence is accumulating from various quarters that cancer cells possess as complete a complement of "information" as normal cells: for example, some bronchial carcinomas actually produce ACTH, a pituitary hormone[24]. In normal cells of a given tissue, only a small fraction of the DNA (histone-free ?) is likely to be in use to pass on information via messenger RNA. From observations on the histone: DNA ratio it has been suggested that with neoplasia the output of information is reduced[103]. The first step in the neoplastic transformation, not sufficient in itself to produce neoplasia, may well be irreversible[40], but it is doubtful whether observed effects of carcinogens on actual DNA molecules (Chapter 3) are relevant even to the action of the carcinogens in question. Undoubtedly, however, alterations in DNA expression must play some part in neoplasia, and should feature in any hypothesis even if the centre of the stage is held not by DNA itself but by other constituents such as histones or messenger RNA.

In a hypothesis put forward by Busch[14], altered function of DNA is the primary event: virtually all cells contain a "cancer DNA", from which the normal suppressor is displaced in consequence of combination between the carcinogen and DNA. This displacement may occur either immediately after exposure to carcinogen, or following the intervention of a promoting factor (whereby the latent period is explained). In the "stage of acceleration" the cancer DNA, now unsuppressed, would form "cancer RNA", and thence "cancer protein" which in turn would fit as a co-factor on to DNA and accelerate the formation of cancer RNA — and so on. In support of this hypothesis there is adduced evidence from Busch's laboratory (cf. ref. 16) on abnormalities in RNA and nuclear proteins in tumours — notably in the Walker tumour. Even in genetically slanted studies it seems desirable that tumours should be compared with *homologous* normal tissues.

Deep exploration of this somewhat fanciful hypothesis is obviously beyond the range of present-day techniques — the "cancer DNA" being supposedly a single, very small genetic locus. With no less plausibility it can be suggested, as a variant of this hypothesis, that in cancer there is re-activation (de-repression) of a *normal* DNA locus or loci which, in the early history of the particular tissue or of the species, mediated cell multiplication — perhaps a "dormant gene" in the sense used by L. Pauling.

Must the neoplastic transformation directly concern nucleic acids? The idea of a direct alteration of the genetic apparatus by carcinogens, as in the hypothesis of Busch, is admittedly compatible with evidence that some carcinogens can alter nucleic acids, but is circumvented in certain other hypotheses which may be termed "genotypic" as distinct from "genetic". Theories centered on RNA templates in the cytoplasm (see above) are essentially genotypic rather than genetic; but mechanisms are conceivable which do not centre on nucleic acids, even cytoplasmic. Thus, on the basis of autoradiographic studies which, although thorough, were done with a limited and unhappily chosen range of tissues, Seed[179] postulated that in tumour cells there is *continuous* formation of nuclear protein and RNA (their formation being normally a concomitant of DNA replication, perhaps requiring some separation of DNA strands); by virtue of "deletion or mismatching of a growth-controlling protein normally associated with the double-stranded DNA" the latter supposedly becomes an effective template.

In Madison, home of the original "deletion hypothesis" as later revised by Potter[8], a revision from a different angle has been suggested[39] in the light of newer genetic concepts such as are summarized in Fig. 12. It is argued that the carcinogen could inactivate the repressor produced by a regulator and permit synthesis, via a structural gene, of a normally repressed enzyme; the product of the enzyme reaction would itself act at an even earlier stage of the control mechanism and *prevent* renewed production of the repressor. In an alternative scheme[39] for perpetuation of enzyme synthesis via a normally repressed structural gene, the initial action of the carcinogen is similar, but there is concomitant activation of a second *regulator* gene (through the same operator gene), the repressor from which maintains the carcinogen-induced block of the regulator gene more immediately concerned with synthesis of the enzyme. In these ingenious speculations, the supposed processes could be cytoplasmic and, moreover, would be self-perpetuating — which explains why the carcinogen need be present only initially. The latent period is still puzzling; but an explanation might be sought on lines suggested by W. S. Bullough[21] (cf. H. S. Kaplan[21]) — that small groups of cells which, through carcinogen action, have lost the normal "chalone" which inhibits mitosis and de-differentiation are for a time held in check by chalone diffusing from adjoining normal cells; neoplasia would ensue "when the few cells which had completely lost their power to produce chalone formed a group large enough to escape from the influences of their neighbours".

In years to come, more definite information should become available on endogenous agents which, perhaps through transfer from one cell to another, supposedly control growth and differentiation, on lines suggested by (*inter alia*) S. Cohen[43], H. S. Kaplan[21], E. E. Osgood, A. Szent-Györgyi[192] and S. Yasuda[209]. It may indeed be an over-simplification to view cancer essentially as accelerated cell division amenable to analysis by biochemical study of large cell populations, and explicable in terms of bottlenecks restraining DNA synthesis or other present-day metabolic concepts. Cancer arising in tissues which, unlike liver, normally contain many proliferating cells might represent the division, at a normal rate, of those daughter cells which would normally *fail* to divide (cf. E. V. Cowdry[7], H. S. Kaplan[21]). However, with the advent of experimental tumours of "minimum-deviation" type, the idea that a given cell has two alternative fates — to multiply or to differentiate — has become a rather unprofitable line of thought.

CHAPTER 9

Biochemical Pharmacology

THE classical methods of treating cancer patients, by irradiation or by surgical extirpation of the tumour, are often successful if applied before metastases have formed. A recent variant of the surgical approach, pioneered by C. Huggins in Chicago[23] and successful in certain breast cancers, is the removal or destruction of endocrine glands concerned in the production of oestrogens (ovaries, adrenals, pituitary). With the hope of developing treatments less traumatic to the patients and more consistently effective, enormous effort is now being devoted to searches for anti-cancer drugs. It has been argued that too little effort is being devoted to the discovery of basic biochemical facts requisite for the rational development of drugs, and too much effort to the trial of chemical variants of the few drugs already in the therapeutic armoury.

The author does not share the pessimism expressed in some quarters concerning the future prospects of cancer chemotherapy. Nevertheless, the main theme in the vast literature is disappointment which, however, is sometimes a reflection of slipshod animal experimentation. The following survey is necessarily too brief to do justice to the importance of the topic (see, for example, refs. 3, 32).

Chemotherapeutic Agents

In summary, the growth of at least some types of animal tumours can be inhibited by various chemical agents, including certain hormones, folate analogues, alkylating agents, alkaloids, and antibiotics such as actinomycin D and mitomycin C. Such agents, of which a selection is listed below in Table 8, will be considered from the viewpoint of their mode of action rather than of their clinical applications. Only well evaluated drugs will be considered, although there are already hints of future developments — for example, the suppression of tumour growth in animals by ill-defined agents such as "retine"[192] or RNA preparations[16] (cf. M. C. Niu[32,43,54]), or the prevention of chemical carcinogenesis or tumour growth in animals by "immunoprophylaxis" (J. H. F. Maisin[31,32,132]; I. N. Maisky *et al.*[32]) or by supplementation of the diet with, for example, riboflavin or choline (Le Breton and Moulé[12]).

A few of the chemically defined agents that can arrest the growth of animal tumours are effective against certain human cancers, particularly leukaemias. However, the arrest is usually transient because of the appearance of resistance to the drug. A further difficulty is that even the least toxic drugs may cause damage to rapidly proliferating cells other than cancer cells, notably in the intestinal epithelium and bone marrow (Burchenal[3]).

As an example of how hormone-dependent tumours may respond to hormone administration (Segaloff[3]), mention may be made of the use of stilboestrol to suppress cancer of the prostate — an organ which is normally dependent on endogenous androgens. Oestrogens are likewise effective against certain breast cancers, paradoxical though this may seem in view of the above-mentioned surgical approach to breast cancer. Some neoplasms of lymphoid tissue, which may be collectively described as the lymphoproliferative disorders, may respond to adrenocorticoid-type steroids such as cortisone, prednisone or 9-α-fluorocorticoids (W. Jacobson[19]), this action being in accord with the involution caused in normal lymphatic tissues by adrenocortical hormones. Radio-iodine in high dosage may destroy thyroid tumours, the thyroid being an efficient "iodine trap". Such examples of tissue selectivity in drug uptake are all too few.

Alkylating agents illustrate the apparent paradox (Chapter 3) that the same compound may either produce or arrest tumours, depending on dosage and other conditions. These agents, despite their toxicity, are widely used in certain leukaemias and are of considerable value in controlling the activity of the disease, especially in chronic granulocytic and chronic lymphocytic leukaemia. Certain acute leukaemias are said to respond to 6-azauridine, and certain solid tumours (notably of the breast and gastro-intestinal tract) have some susceptibility to 5-fluorouracil. The latter agents are examples of drugs patterned on nucleotide precursors. One such drug, 6-uracil-methylsulphone, also acts as an alkylating agent. Drugs such as methotrexate, which impairs nucleotide synthesis by acting as an antimetabolite of folate (see below), are effective against acute leukaemia of childhood and certain solid tumours.

Tissue Metabolism in Relation to Drug Action

For some anti-cancer drugs there is, at least in retrospect, a biochemical rationale, usually in terms of inhibition (ideally non-competitive) of essential enzymes or of "fraudulent" behaviour as an enzyme substrate such that products are formed which block the multiplication of target cells. However, the first question that has to be considered is how to attain the ideal situation of a high concentration of the active form of the agent within cancer cells but not normal cells.

Uptake and metabolic transformations of drugs. Observations that cancer cells are particularly effective in taking up administered uracil were the foundation for the development of the fluoro-pyrimidines as anti-tumour agents (Heidelberger[3]); with azauridine there is notable selectivity towards cancer cells. Selective uptake by cancer cells also tends to occur with anti-folates (Werkheiser[3]). In connection with the efficacy of purine and folate antagonists in myeloid leukaemia but allegedly not in lymphatic leukaemia, W. Willmanns (cf. ref. 183) has suggested that whereas in the former condition there is accelerated formation of purines and of the thymine methyl group, in lymphocytes nucleotide synthesis may occur predominantly from pre-formed bases or nucleosides (e.g. thymidine) through "salvage" pathways which would be unaffected by the agents.

Only limited selectivity in uptake has so far been achieved with approaches such as "regional perfusion" (intravascular administration, confined as far as possible to the tumour area) or the introduction into the molecule of a "protective group" which, by virtue of the tendency of cancer cells to have a low pH (Chapter 5), might be hydrolysed therein and liberate the active agent (W. C. J. Ross[32,42]). R. E. Parks[3] suggests that the low pH of tumours favours selective attack by pyrimidine analogues such as 5-fluoro-uracil, these analogues being more reactive in an acidic environment. On the grounds that "several types of neoplastic tissue have a relatively lower content of factors concerned with electron transport", Ross[32] has also advocated the trial of known drugs structurally modified so as to be readily oxidized *in vivo* and thereby inactivated in normal cells.

Another approach to getting selective uptake is to attach drugs to antibodies against tumour-specific antigens or, alternatively, to use antibodies containing radio-iodine in high concentration (B. Cinader, D. Pressman[1]). Promising results have been obtained by Pressman with modified antibodies towards fibrin, which is laid down rapidly in malignant tumours. (A variant of this approach, suggested by Pressman, is the use of labelled antibodies to establish the localization of metastases and thereby help the surgeon.) As already mentioned, the problem of selectivity is less serious when it is a matter of treating endocrine-gland or hormone-dependent tumours.

Once the drug has entered the cell, it is likely to undergo metabolic transformation which may result in either activation or deactivation. The conversion of pyrimidine analogues into the corresponding ribonucleotides, which apparently mediate the anti-tumour action, may proceed by a pyrophosphorylase pathway, or by a phosphorylase-kinase pathway; the latter at least may have elevated activity in tumours (Chapter 7, Fig. 11). Actual administration of the nucleotide, chemical synthesis of which presents difficulties, is likely to be of no advantage, or even futile because of poor uptake by cells.

Catabolic transformations resulting in loss of the drug should ideally be minimal in the target cells, and are relevant to the question of toxicity. Thus, LePage[3] suggests that the high level of guanase found in intestinal epithelium but not in tumours explains the low toxicity of 6-thioguanine. Guanase activity may likewise determine the effectiveness of 8-azaguanine (T. C. Hall *et al.*[13]). For 6-mercaptopurine, some potentiation due to suppression of catabolism has been achieved by concomitant administration of 4-hydroxypyrazolo-(3,4-*d*)pyridimine, an inhibitor of xanthine oxidase (G. B. Elion and colleagues[3]). In respect of 5-fluorouracil, which is degraded by the same pathway as for uracil, certain animal tumours were found in Heidelberger's laboratory[3] to have the merit of a poor degradative capacity, unlike the hepatomas mentioned in Chapter 7.

The efficacy of 6-thioguanine in certain leukaemias has been attributed[135] to rapid conversion into the nucleotide — the pyrophosphorylase being much higher in bone marrow (which uses pre-formed purines from elsewhere) than in intestinal mucosa — and to a relatively low extent of catabolism to 6-thio-uric acid.

Choice of enzymic targets. Mention may first be made of an enzymic target for prophylactic as distinct from chemotherapeutie treatment: inhibition of β-glucuronidase by saccharolactone has been advocated by E. Boyland[9,48] as a means of averting bladder cancer, on grounds which will be evident from observations on 2-naphthylamine mentioned in Chapter 3. Also worthy of mention, as future hope for chemotherapy, is the idea of searching for an agent that will rupture lysosomes — and thus cause devastating liberation of stored hydrolases — in cancer cells but not normal cells (C. de Duve[19]; cf. A. C. Allison[55]; J. A. Lucy[43]).

One chemotherapeutic approach is directed towards inhibiting specific enzymes (perhaps after initial "fraudulent" acceptance of the agent by an enzyme farther back in the line), rather than towards deranging the genetic machinery in ways to be discussed later. Enzymes which show *high* activity in cancer cells can, as already indicated, be exploited to achieve conversion of the drug into an active agent within the cell, but are hardly ideal targets for chemotherapy by enzyme inhibition since normal cells might well be preferentially destroyed. For enzymes which show *low* activity in cancer cells, the question has seldom been posed whether one should attempt to raise the activity towards normal, or to obliterare the activity and hope that the abundance of the enzyme in normal cells will enable them to survive any partial loss. The latter course assumes that the enzyme concerned is vital to the life of the cancer cell — which is unlikely to hold for many of the enzymes stated in preceding chapters to be low in hepatomas or other tumours. Except for the following digression, the enzymic approaches now to be mentioned centre on blocking activity (not always that of enzymes that are already low).

The opposite course, aimed at restoration of depressed enzymic activities towards normal by therapy with enzyme preparations (necessarily heterologous), has already been tried out, notably by G. de Lamirande[9]. Injections of xanthine oxidase may arrest the growth of mammary tumours in mice. The growth of certain tumours, especially ascitic, was retarded by glutaminase, but only transiently[101]. The trial of catalase as an anti-tumour agent met with no success (R. N. Feinstein & M. Vetter, 1961[20]). Pancreatic preparations (impure ?) of RNAase and especially of DNAase have sometimes shown promise (see ref. 130), even though tumours are quite rich in nucleases (Chapter 7). The inhibitory effect on ascites-cell growth of actinomycin D and RNAase given together surpassed that obtained with either given alone[176].

Surprising though it may seem, enzyme molecules can enter cells (perhaps by pinocytosis or "endocytosis") without loss of activity, as has been demonstrated both for RNAase (L. Ledoux) and for xanthine oxidase (G. de Lamirande); but it now appears that the uptake of xanthine oxidase in mammary tumours or liver is mainly by reticulo-endothelial cells[89]. "Enzyme chemotherapy" is a long way from being a practical proposition as distinct from a curiosity.

To guide the choice of enzymic targets for chemotherapy, information is needed on enzyme levels not only in tumours but also in a *range* of normal tissues as distinct from the homologous normal tissues considered in previous chapters. The information so far available[20,25] is rather discouraging, in that few enzymes in tumours show activities outside the wide range covered by normal tissues.

Agents affecting energy metabolism. Inhibition of anaerobic glycolysis has been observed with alkylating agents *in vitro*, but not with anti-tumour antibiotics[138] with the possible exception of "carcinophilin" (C. G. Schmidt[32]). Busch[14] was able to inhibit lactate dehydrogenase with halogenated pyruvic acids, e.g. $FCH_2.CO.CO_2H$; but — not surprisingly — there was inhibition of pyruvate oxidation in normal as well as in tumour cells, and furthermore there was toxicity towards the central nervous system. Lactate dehydrogenase hardly seems an ideal target since its activity is of the normal order in many tumours; but further trials may be warranted[97a].

M. B. Sahasrabudhe and colleagues[32,173] have devoted attention to analogues of 6-phosphogluconate (e.g. thiodiglycollate), prompted by the apparent importance of the hexose monophosphate pathway for the energy requirements of tumours. Good results have so far been obtained only with ascitic tumours, with which the problem of poor vascularity does not arise. The anti-tumour action of bisguanyl-hydrazones (E. Mihich[3]) and of certain other agents[138] might in part be due to interference with oxidative phosphorylation. Observations in the late R. K. Morton's laboratory[13] may offer promise: they concern blockage of NAD synthesis (cf. C. G. Schmidt[32]) by 6-mercaptopurine *in vitro*, with formation of a "fraudulent" NAD. For phthalanilides, inhibition of lipid synthesis may be the mode of action[94].

Agents affecting nucleic-acid structure or synthesis. At the end of Chapter 3, mention was made of chemical modifications induced by alkylating agents in nucleic acids and also in proteins. In accordance with such observations, altered chromatographic behaviour of leucocyte DNA has been seen in leukaemic patients treated with myleran (busulphan)[86]. However, DNA preparations from ascites cells grown in mice given nitrogen mustard showed no abnormality other than a high protein content[97]. A. Lindner and colleagues[16] have shown histochemically a rise in the histone: DNA ratio of ascites cells after administration of fluoro-uracil.

Certain anti-tumour agents can produce altered nucleic acids through fraudulent incorporation of the agent (Table 8). An interesting feature of the incorporation of 5-iodo-uridine into RNA is that the cells are rendered more sensitive to destruction by irradiation (W. Szyabalski[8], A. D. Welch *et al.*[16]).

Alterations thus produced in the genetic machinery — with consequences such as production of faulty enzyme proteins[13] — might well be one mechanism underlying not only the production of tumours (Chapter 3) but also their obliteration, provided that the alterations are minimal in normal cells. However, the reservation must be made that the alterations are very small in extent. Thus, with alkylating agents *in vivo* the alterations may, as a rough average, affect only one base per DNA molecule (see end of Chapter 3), and moreover the extent of alteration is not correlated with the susceptibility of the tumour to the agent[194] (see also Warwick[3]).

For at least some anti-tumour agents, the mechanism underlying their action is probably inhibition of the synthesis of nucleic acids, not necessarily through fraudulent incorporation. Examples of such inhibition, produced in diverse ways, are shown in Table 8; but a warning given previously (Chapters 2 and 7) must be reiterated — that a reduced incorporation as tabulated does not prove decreased nucleic-acid synthesis unless, as has seldom been the case, the precursor pool has been checked for a possible change in specific radioactivity. It should further be pointed out that an actual enhancement of glycine incorporation into RNA (with a concurrent reduction in DNA labelling) was observed by S. N. Pradhan and W. L. West[32] in experiments with a phosphoramide, tris(1-aziridinyl)phosphine sulphide (thioTEPA); this

TABLE 8. BEHAVIOUR OF ANTI-TUMOUR DRUGS IN RELATION TO NUCLEIC ACIDS

In general the effects tabulated were demonstrated *in vivo*, or else *in vitro* with whole-cell preparations from drug-treated animals, and refer to "target" tissues (susceptible tumours, or normal tissues homologous with susceptible tumours). For pyrimidine analogues in particular, there is usually an initial transformation of the agent into its nucleotide (see text). Where no full reference is cited, refs. 3, 13 and 16 may be consulted.

Agent	Behaviour	Main authors
	Pyrimidine analogues	
6-Azauridine (*AUR*)	Inhibits conversion of orotate into UMP and also into pseudouridine (as present in "soluble RNA")	R. E. Handschumacher
5-Fluorouracil (*FU*); similar results with 5-fluoro-2′-deoxy-uridine (*FUDR*) and 5-fluoro-orotic acid (*FO*)	Inhibits of incorporation of orotate or uracil into RNA, of orotate into DNA (thymine), and especially of formate into DNA. Itself incorporated into RNA. *FO* but not *FU* reduces the pseudouridine content of "soluble RNA"	C. Heidelberger[16,121], P. Reichard[162]
5-iododeoxyuridine (*IUDR*)	Inhibits incorporation of thymidine into DNA. Incorporated into DNA	W. H. Prusoff, A. D. Welch[16]
6-uracil-methylsulphone (*UMS*; an alkylating agent)	Inhibits incorporation of precursors into DNA, apparently by blocking conversion of ribonucleotides into deoxyribonucleotides	E. H. Creaser[81]
	Purine analogues	
8-Azaguanine; 2,6-diaminopurine	Inhibit incorporation of formate into nucleic-acid purines. Incorporated into nucleic acids (as if guanine, in case of diaminopurine); no azaguanine in microsomal RNA	H. E. Skipper; see also [181,206]
6-Mercaptopurine (*MP*)	Inhibits purine biosynthesis. Itself perhaps slightly incorporated into DNA and RNA	R. W. Brockman; G. H. Hitchings[52]

6-Thioguanine (2-amino-6-mercaptopurine)	Reduces *in vitro* incorporation of uracil (not of guanine) into DNA and microsomal RNA. Itself incorporated into DNA and RNA	D. H. Adams[52]; G. A. LePage
	Folate or glutamine anti-metabolites	
Anti-folates, e.g. methotrexate [*ME*; amethopterin; 4-amino-(4-deoxy)-N^{10}-methyl-pteroylglutamate]	Inhibit formation of purines and of DNA thymine (by "stoichiometric" inhibition of dihydrofolate reductase)	J. R. Bertino; J. F. Holland; W. L. Werkheiser; R. J. Winzler
Azaserine (*AS*; *O*-diazo--acetyl-L-serine), 6-diazo-5-oxo-norleucine (*DAON*)	Inhibit incorporation of precursors into nucleic-acid cytosine; but *AS* may enhance guanine or uracil incorporation into DNA and RNA	D. H. Adams[52]; M. L. Eidinoff; R. B. Hurlbert[110]
	Alkylating agents (see also end of Chapter 3)	
"Mustards", e.g. Nitrogen mustard (*HN*2), sulphur mustard	Variable effects, sometimes biphasic and possibly non-specific, on incorporation of precursors into nucleic acids; mononucleotide formation probably unaffected. Themselves may be slightly incorporated into DNA, but hardly affect its physical properties	Y. Miura[138]; E. G. Trams [194]; authors cited in [156] (Davidson, Goldthwait, Lawrence & Carter); R. H. Golder *et al.*[97]
Other agents, e.g. chlorambucil, myleran (busulphan), thioTEPA, urethane (*U*), "Uracil mustard"	Inhibit incorporation of precursors into nucleic acids (not consistently found with myleran; stimulation may be found for RNA with thioTHEPA — see text). Formation of pyridimine moieties unaffected by urethane. Myleran may alter DNA properties	B. Byvoet & H. Busch[13a]; Di Mayorca *et al.*[86]; M. E. Eidinoff; S. N. Pradhan[32, 156]; E. G. Trams[194]; R. J. Winzler; cf. S. Rogers [77,163]
	Other types of agent	
Phthalanilides	Inhibit incorporation of precursors into nucleic acids	C. J. Kensler
9-a-Fluorocortisone	Inhibits formate incorporation into DNA	C. Heidelberger[121]
Actinomycin D	Inhibits DNA-dependent RNA synthesis; reduces RNA level, especially if RNAase also injected	E. Reich; A. C. Sartorelli [176] (*inter alia*)

enhancement, which was not confined to any particular type of RNA, was thought to be a compensatory response to arrested synthesis of cytoplasmic protein.

In general, however, the tabulated findings suggest reduced nucleic-acid synthesis, of both DNA and RNA or at least of DNA alone or RNA alone; the type of RNA affected has seldom been investigated. Among the diverse metabolic effects of 5-fluorouracil (Table 8), C. Heidelberger[3] attaches particular importance to the apparent inhibition of DNA synthesis, this inhibition being attributable to competitive inhibition of dTMP synthesis. Inhibition of dTMP synthesis likewise underlies the action of the anti-folates, for which dihydrofolate reductase has a very high affinity[36]. It is uncertain what importance should be attached to findings of reduced activity of duplicase (DNA polymerase) in cells exposed to 5-iododeoxyuridine (Prusoff[3]) or to prednisolone[60]

For agents which influence pyrimidine metabolism and for which the enzymic steps that can be affected are known, the information available concerning inhibition (denoted by diagonal bars) as distinct from "fraudulent incorporation" may be summarized thus, the abbreviations for agents being as in Table 8 (except for *UMS*, uracil-methylsulphone):

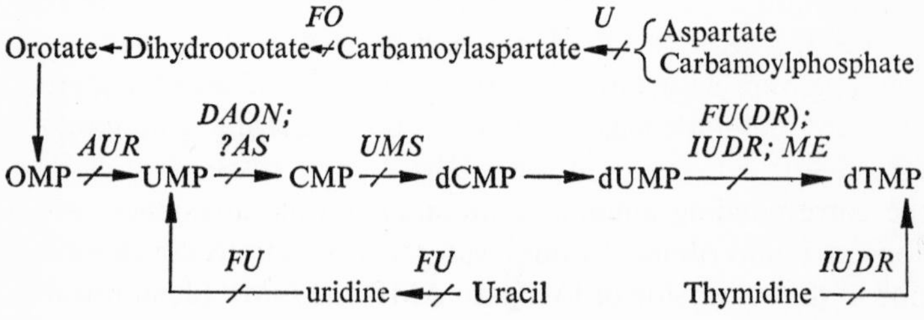

These various inhibitions (the character of which will not be discussed here) cannot all be assumed to have a bearing on overall effects of the agents on nucleic-acid synthesis.

The reactions leading to orotate (as studied in the laboratories of E. Bresnick[13,47] and L. H. Smith[163]) would be particularly difficult to render rate-limiting in tumours, and it is doubtful if any significance should be attached to inhibitions observed with urethane and with other agents not shown. In some instances, as in the case of inhibition of aspartate transcarbamoylase by *IUDR*, very high concentrations of the agent have been used *in vitro* to demonstrate inhibition. Certain leukaemic cells, however, seem to be so highly dependent on the *de novo* pathway that it can be fatally impaired by aza-uridine (*AUR*) in therapeutic doses — this agent, as its ribonucleotide, competing with OMP for orotidylate decarboxylase (R. E. Handschumacher[13]; cf. T. Sorm and J. Skoda[32]). In connection with the inhibitory effect of fluoro-orotic acid (*FO*) on dihydro-orotate synthesis (E. Bresnick[13,47]), it should be pointed out that this agent is inferior to fluorouracil (*FU*) with respect to ability to inhibit tumour growth at non-toxic dose levels.

Agents such as uracil-methylsulphone (*UMS*) and myleran are without effect on the *de novo* pathway to UMP. It is in fact fortunate, in relation to future broadening of the drug spectrum, that there are diverse mechanisms by which nucleic-acid synthesis can be inhibited. New agents to block the supply of dTMP and other deoxyribonucleotides might prove especially useful.

Inhibition of purine biosynthesis (and hence of nucleic-acid synthesis) can be achieved not only by reducing the supply of methyl groups with anti-folates[36], but also by the use of azaserine or diazo-oxo-norleucine to block steps requiring glutamine — notably the conversion of formylglycinamide ribonucleotide into the corresponding amidine compound. Purine analogues, when converted into ribonucleotides, can cause pseudo-feedback inhibition of the conversion of IMP into AMP and GMP (demonstrable with mercaptopurine, at least at high levels[57]), and of the condensation of phosphoribosylpyrophosphate (PRPP) and glutamine to give phosphoribosylamine (demonstrable with mercaptopurine, thioguanine, azaguanine, and also glutamine anti-metabolites[3,13,57]). From experiments in which normal or leukaemic leucocytes were incubated with labelled adenine or guanine in the presence of diaminopurine, it appears that this agent can block the conversion of GMP into AMP but not the conversion of AMP into GMP; with adenine the labelling of nucleic-acid adenine was unaffected, and with guanine the labelling of nucleic-acid guanine was slightly depressed[181].

Enhancement of nucleic-acid catabolism could, of course, have the same net result as inhibition of synthesis, and might well play a role in the above-mentioned anti-tumour effects of nuclease preparations. Mitomycin C seems to cause depolymerisation of DNA through DNAase action[13]. The fall in RNA in a lymphosarcoma regressing under the influence of 9-α-fluoroprednisolone was preceded by a rise in acid-RNAase activity[130]. Unfortunately, the conditions for assay of the latter were probably such as to rupture lysosomes and show total activity, as distinct from the free activity that perhaps governs RNA catabolism; the stability of lysosomes may actually be increased by certain adrenocorticoids (de Duve[19]; Jacobson[19]).

For the anti-tumour actions of steroids there are, however, likely to be loci besides acid RNAase; thus, reduced activity of the leucocyte enzymes concerned in synthesis of dTMP (from thymidine) and of DNA has been observed in leukaemic patients treated with prednisone[60]. Possible loci in the area of amino-acid metabolism are suggested by the observation that a rise in transaminase activity, towards alanine or tyrosine, occurs in Walker tumours regressing under treatment with cortisol, although not with alkylating agents (F. Rosen[3]).

Agents affecting protein structure or synthesis. Fluorouracil can apparently give rise to abnormal enzyme proteins[13] — a finding which recalls results obtained with alkylating agents (see end of Chapter 3). Moreover, A. Lindner and colleagues[16] have reported that in ascites cells from mice treated with fluoro-uracil there is a fall in protein-bound —SH with a rise in —S—S—. In leucocytes from patients with leukaemia (chronic granulocytic) responding to myleran or X-irradiation, there was a fall in non-protein —SH, but the —S—S— level also showed some depression[104] (cf. G. Rouser *et al.*[28]). Emmelot[13a] has speculated that alkylating agents such as myleran may abolish active transport (e.g. of Na^+ ions) by interacting with —SH groups in the plasma membrane.

Certain anti-tumour drugs perhaps act by interfering with protein synthesis, not necessarily by way of a derangement produced in the nucleic-acid area. Inhibition of amino-acid incorporation into protein *in vivo* has been observed with various agents, for example phosphoramides and other alkylating agents[138,156,194], bisguanylhydrazones (E.Mihich[3]), phthalanilides (C. J. Kensler[3]), azaguanine[13], thioguanine[52] and azaserine[52]. Nuclear proteins showed a markedly depressed uptake of labelled arginine in rats given 5-bis(2-chloroethyl)aminouracil[14], but the converse was usually found (both for histones and for non-histone nuclear proteins) in lymphosarcoma-bearing mice given thioTEPA (S. N. Pradhan and W. L. West[32]). In the latter study the incorporation into cytoplasmic proteins was strikingly depressed.

Reduced incorporation as in the examples mentioned does not, of course, prove that protein synthesis was reduced, particularly since the amino-acid pool is sometimes affected by cytotoxic agents (G. Rouser *et al.*[28]; cf. E. Roberts and D. G. Simonsen[28]). However, in a study of tryptophan pyrrolase (S. Gaetani and M. A. Spandoni[13]) it appeared that enzyme induction was reduced after administration of fluoro-uracil.

Little effort has been made in studies of amino-acid incorporation to ascertain how the apparent changes in protein synthesis were brought about, and there has been no study subtle enough to allow of any assertion that protein synthesis may be a primary locus of action for anti-tumour drugs. There have been speculations that the ability of microsomal RNA to accept amino-acids (bound to transfer RNA) is impaired by thioguanine[52] — although "fraudulent RNA" is usually absent from microsomes — and that "coding sites" on nucleic acids are blocked by phthalanilides (C. J. Kensler[3]), although inhibition of lipid synthesis by the latter seems to be more important than inhibition of protein synthesis[94]. Interaction with DNA is of course, well established for the actinomycins (E. Reich[3]; cf. Fig. 12), but with mitomycin C the depolymerization of DNA is not immediately followed by a derangement of protein synthesis[13]. Inhibition of amino-acid incorporation into "soluble RNA" has been demonstrated *in vitro* with nitrogen mustard or chromomycin A_3 by Y. Miura and colleagues[138], and with 6-aza-uridine-5′-diphosphate by I. Rychlik[13]; but formation of the latter diphosphate from aza-uridine may not occur in mammalian tissues as distinct from bacteria (Prusoff[3]). At least for agents such as azaguanine and mercaptopurine, interference with the GTP-mediated incorporation of amino-acids into protein on ribosomes has been considered unlikely[13].

Some workers have, rather uncritically, incubated tissue samples with drugs, rather than injected the drugs. Studies with drugs *in vitro*, as with carcinogens, are fraught with uncertainty especially since the active form of the agent in the animal might be a metabolite not readily formed *in vitro*. The old-fashioned approach of injecting the agent and *then* studying the tissue *in vivo* or *in vitro* is most likely to pay dividends in the form of meaningful results. Ideally the dosage should be pharmacological rather toxological, the tissues studied should include the target tissue, and inactive analogues should also be tested. Patient work on these lines should enable primary effects to be discerned among the diverse metabolic effects commonly demonstrable with anti-tumour drugs. Concerning this embarrassing diversity, it is refreshing to read in connection with one class of agent (Vinca alkaloids; I. S. Johnson and collaborators[3]) that "Biochemical studies to date do not reveal any effect on cellular respiration, glycolysis, protein or nucleic acid synthesis".*

Drug Resistance

The term "drug resistance" in the present context means that an individual tumour which at first responded has become insensitive, or that a tumour differs from other tumours, supposedly similar in

* Recently, however, inhibition of incorporation of uridine into RNA and of valine into protein has been observed, with ascites cells *in vivo*. Creasey, W. A. & Markiw, M. E. (1964). *Biochim. biophys. Acta*, **87**, 601.

References

Economy of references has been achieved by using text references to Books, Reviews and Symposia wherever possible, and by restricting citation of actual papers to recent ones even where earlier work from the laboratory in question is being discussed. Such papers are cited *in italics* where the work under discussion is from a different laboratory and is merely quoted in the paper. As an alternative means of tracking down original references, use may be made of Author Indices (preferably Cumulative Indices) in *Chemical Abstracts* or other abstracts.

Books, Reviews and Symposia

Note: In general, information on a particular topic can often be tracked down by perusal of:

Advances in Cancer Research
Advances in Enzyme Regulation
Annual Review of Biochemistry
Progress in Experimental Tumor Research
Hirschberg, E. (1957). *Cancer Research*, **17,** 77 (List of reviews)

Items marked with an asterisk (*) are particularly recommended for general orientation.

1. [No editor] (1963). *Canad. Cancer Conf.*, **5,** 1–479. Various topics.
2. [No editor] (1951). *Cancer Res.*, **11,** 565–602. Symposium, Intermediary carbohydrate metabolism in tumor tissue.
3. [No editor] (1963). *Cancer Res.*, **23,** 1181–497. Symposium, "Problems basic to cancer chemotherapy.
4. [No editor] (1962). *Il Cancro*, **15,** 139–267. Symposium on leukaemic cells.
5. [No editor] (1956). *Science*, **124,** 267–72. On respiratory impairment in cancer cells.

*6. Aisenberg, A. C. (1961). *The Glycolysis and Respiration of Tumors*, 224 pp. (New York: Academic Press).

7. M. D. Anderson Hospital and Tumor Institute (1960). *Cell Physiology of Neoplasia*, 653 pp. (Austin: Univ. of Texas Press).
8. M. D. Anderson Hospital and Tumor Institute (1962). *Molecular Basis of Neoplasia*, 614 pp. (Austin: Univ. of Texas Press).
9. BERGEL, F. (1961). *Chemistry of Enzymes in Cancer*, 122 pp. (Springfield, Ill.: C. C. Thomas).
10. BOXER, G. E. & DEVLIN, T. M. (1961). *Science*, **134**, 1495–1501. Pathways of intracellular hydrogen transport.
*11. BOYLAND, E. [editor] (1964). *Brit. Med. Bull.*, **20**, 87–170 [see also **14**, 73–192] — Mechanisms of carcinogenesis: Chemical, physical and viral.
*12. BRACHET, J. & MIRSKY, A. E. [editors] (1961). *The Cells*, Vol. 5, 597 pp. (New York: Academic Press).
13. BROCKMAN, R. W. & ANDERSON, E. (1963). *Ann. Rev. Biochem.*, **32**, 463–512. Biochemistry of cancer (metabolic aspects).
13a. BUFFA, P. [editor] (1964). *From Molecule to Cell*: Symposium on Electron Microscopy, (Rome: Consiglio Nazionale delle Ricerche).
14. BUSCH, H. (1962). *An Introduction to the Biochemistry of the Cancer Cell*, 424 pp. (New York: Academic Press).
15. BUSCH, H. (1963). *Cancer Res.*, **23**, 313–39. The nucleolus of the cancer cell: A review.
16. BUSCH, H. [editor] (1963). *The Nucleus of the Cancer Cell*, *Exptl. Cell Res.*, *Suppl.* **9**, 571 pp.; published as a book (New York: Academic Press).
16a. BUSCH, H. & STARBUCK, W. C. (1964). *Ann. Rev. Biochem.*, **33**, 519–70. Biochemistry of cancer.
17. CARRUTHERS, C. (1950). *Cancer Res.*, **10**, 255–65 (cf. p. 636). Chemical studies on the transformation of mouse epidermis to squamous cell carcinoma: A review.
*18. CLAYSON, D. B. (1962). *Chemical Carcinogenesis*, 467 pp. (London: J. & A. Churchill).
18a. DAVIDSON, J. N. (1963). Royal Inst. of Chem. Lect. Series, No. 1, 17 pp. *Living Molecules*.
19. DE REUCK, A. V. S. & KNIGHT, J. [editors] (1964). *Cellular Injury* (Ciba Foundation Symposium), 403 pp. (London: J. & A. Churchill).
20. DOUGLAS, W. R. (1963). *Brit. J. Cancer*, **17**, 415–45. Relationships of enzymology to cancer: A review.
21. EMMELOT, P. & MÜHLBOCK, O. [editors] (1964). *Cellular Control Mechanisms and Cancer*, 387 pp. (Amsterdam: Elsevier).
*22. FARBER, E. (1963). *Adv. Cancer Res.*, **7**, 383–465. Ethionine carcinogenesis.
*23. FURTH, J. (1961). *Fed. Proc.*, **20**, 865–73. Vistas in the etiology and pathogenesis of tumors.
*24. GELLHORN, A. (1963). *Cancer Res.*, **23**, 961–70. The unifying thread.
25. GREENSTEIN, J. P. (1954). *Biochemistry of Cancer*, 2nd edn, 653 pp. (New York: Academic Press).
26. HAVEN, F. L. & BLOOR, W. R. (1956). *Adv. Cancer Res.*, **4**, 238–314. Lipids in cancer.

27. HIEGER, I. (1961). *Carcinogenesis*, 138 pp. (New York: Academic Press).
28. HOLDEN, J. T. [editor] (1962). *Amino Acid Pools*, 815 pp. (Amsterdam: Elsevier).
29. KIT, S. (1960). *Cancer Res.*, **20**, 1121–48. Nucleic acid synthesis in the neoplastic cell and impact of nuclear changes on the biochemistry of tumor tissue: A review.
30. KIT, S. & GRIFFIN, A. C. (1958). *Cancer Res.*, **18**, 621–56. Cellular metabolism and cancer: A review.
31. MAISIN, J. [editor] (1963). *Acta Unio internat. contra Cancrum*, **19**, 1–801. Proc. Cancer Congress: "Immunology and genetics of tumours," "Role of viruses in the origin of cancer", "Carcinogenesis".
32. MAISIN, J. [editor] (1964). *Acta Unio internat. contra Cancrum*, **20**, 1–1858. Proc. Cancer Congress, including: "Chemotherapy", "Aetiology, and pathogenesis of liver cancer", "Biochemistry of cancer", "Biology of the cancer cell", "Tumour host relationships and hormonal status".
33. MANDEL, P. (1964). *Bull. Soc. Chim. biol.*, **46**, 43–70. Quelques aspects de la régulation des biosynthèses des acides ribonucléiques chez les animaux supérieurs.
34. MERCER, E. H. (1961). *Proc. Roy. Soc. Med.*, **54**, 1057–64. The electron microscopy of normal and neoplastic cells.
35. MORRIS, H. P. (1963). *Progr. exptl. Tumor Res.*, **3**, 370–411. Some growth, morphological and biochemical characteristics of hepatoma 5123 and other new transplantable hepatomas.
36. O'BRIEN, J. S. (1962). *Cancer Res.*, **22**, 267–81. The role of the folate coenzymes in cellular division: A review.
*37. PITOT, H. C. (1962). *Fed. Proc.*, **21**, 1124–29. Molecular pathogenesis of experimental liver cancer. [Where this reference is cited, ref. 38 may also be found helpful.]
38. PITOT, H. C. (1964). *Perspectives in Biol. & Med.*, **8**, 50–70 Altered template stability — The molecular mask of malignancy?
39. PITOT, H. C. & HEIDELBERGER, C. (1963). *Cancer Res.*, **23**, 1694–1700. Metabolic regulatory circuits and carcinogenesis.
*40. POTTER, V. R. (1964). *Cancer Res.*, **24**, 1085–98. Biochemical perspectives in cancer research. [See also ref. 21.]
*41. REID, E. (1962). *Cancer Res.*, **22**, 398–430. Significant biochemical effects of hepatocarcinogens in the rat: A review.†
42. ROSS, W. C. J. (1962). *Biological Alkylating Agents*, 232 pp. (London: Butterworths).
43. RUTTER, W. G. [editor] (1964). *Natl. Cancer Inst. Monographs*, **13**, 1–275. Metabolic control mechanisms in animal cells.

† The following errors in this review should be noted:
p. 403, 2nd col., line 4 from foot: mole *should read* μmole;
p. 408, Xanthine oxidase entry, col. 5: (151) *should read* (140);
p. 416, Glucose-6-phosphatase entry, col. 4: (132) *should read* (121);
p. 417, Catalase entry, col. 3: (1–10) *should read* (110);
p. 423, 1st col., line 12: (46) *should read* (36);
p. 423, 2nd col., line 27: (141) *should read* (140).

44. WARBURG, O. (1956). *Science*, **123**, 309–14. On the origin of cancer cells.

*45. WEBER, G. (1961). *Adv. Cancer Res.*, **6**, 403–94. Behaviour of liver enzymes in hepatocarcinogenesis.

46. WEBER, G. [editor] (1963). *Adv. Enzyme Regulation*, **1**, 1–420.

47. WEBER, G. [editor] (1963). *Adv. Enzyme Regulation*, **2**, 1–405.

47a. WEBER, G. [editor] (1965). *Adv. Enzyme Regulation*, **3**, in press.

48. WOLSTENHOLME, G. E. W. & O'CONNOR, C. M. [editors] (1959). *Carcinogenesis* (Ciba Foundation Symposium), 336 pp. (London: J. & A. Churchill).

*49. WRIGHT, G. P. (1958). *An Introduction to Pathology*, 3rd ed., 660 pp. (London: Longmans Green).

50. ZILVERSMIT, D. B. (1960). *Amer. J. Med.*, **29**, 832–48. The design and analysis of isotopic experiments.

Original Papers

51. ABRAHAM, S., CHAIKOFF, I. L. & CADY, P. (1961). *Cancer Res.*, **21**, 938.

52. ADAMS, D. H. (1963). *Biochem. J.*, **89**, 240.

53. ADAMS, H. R. & BUSCH, H. (1962). *Biochem. biophys. res. Commun.*, 9, 578.

54. AKSENOVA, N. N., BRESLER, V. M., VOROB'EV, V. I. & OLENOV, YU. M. (1962). *Tsitologiya*, **4**, 490. Translation (1963) in *Fed. Proc.*, **22**, T1017. Also: (1962). *Nature, Lond.*, **196**, 443.

55. ALLISON, A. C. & MALLUCCI, L. (1964). *Nature, Lond.*, **203**, 1024.

56. ARTAMONOVA, V. A., TIKHONENKO, T. I. & MORGUNOVA, T. D. (1964) *Voprosi Onkologii*, **10**, 22.

56a. BAKAY B. & SOPOZ, S. (1964). *Cancer Res.*, **24**, 1814.

57. BAKER, H. T. & BENNETT, L. L. (1964). *Biochim. biophys. Acta*, **80**, 497.

58. BELFIORE, F. (1962). *Boll. Soc. ital. Biol. sper.*, **38**, 1234. Cited (1964) in *Chem. Abs.*, **60**, 11183.

59. BELOUSOVA, A. M. (1958). *Biokhimia*, **23**, 738.

60. BIANCHI, P. A. (1962). *Biochim. Biophys. Acta*, **55**, 547.

61. BELCHER, M. & WHITE, A. (1958). *J. biol. Chem.*, **233**, 1161.

62. BLOEMENDAL, H., BONT, W. S. & BOSCH, L. (1964). *Cancer Res.*, **24**, 994.

63. BOYLAND, E. & GREEN, B. (1964). *Biochem. J.*, **92**, 4c.

64. BOYLAND, E. & NERY, R. (1965). *Biochem. J.*, **94**, 198.

65. BRESCIANI, F. & AURICCHIO, F. (1962). *Cancer Res.*, **22**, 1284.

66. BRESNICK, E., THOMPSON, U. B., MORRIS, H. P. & LIEBELT, A. G. (1964). *Biochem. biophys. res. Commun.*, **16**, 278.

67. BROOKES, P. & LAWLEY, P. D. (1964). *Nature, Lond.*, **202**, 781.

68. BUCHWALD, M. & BRITTEN, R. J. (1963). *Biophys. J.*, **3**, 155.

69. BURKE, W. T. & MCCOY, J. (1964). *Abstracts, 6th Internat. Congr. Biochem.*, 403.

70. CALCUTT, G. (1958). *Brit. J. Cancer*, **12**, 149.

71. CALCUTT, G. (1964). *Brit. J. Cancer*, **18**, 197.

72. Calcutt, G. & Doxey, D. (1962). *Brit. J. Cancer*, **16**, 806.
73. Canellakis, E. S. (1957). *J. biol. Chem.*, **227**, 701.
74. Carruthers, C. & Heining, A. (1964). *Cancer Res.*, **24**, 485.
75. Carruthers, C. & Suntzeff, V. (1954). *Cancer Res.*, **14**, 29.
76. Cho, Y. S., Pitot, H. C. & Morris, H. P. (1964). *Cancer Res.*, **24**, 52.
77. Chu, E. W. & Malmgren, R. A. (1964). *Cancer Res.*, **24**, 671.
78. Clark, J. B., Greenbaum, A. L., McLean, P. & Reid, E. (1964). *Nature, Lond.*, **201**, 1131.
79. Craddock, V. M. (1964). *Biochem. J.*, **90**, 33P.
80. Creaser, E. H. & Spencer, J. H. (1960). *Biochem. J.*, **76**, 171.
81. Creasey, W. A. & Haff, R. C. (1963). *Cancer Res.*, **23**, 462.
82. Dajani, R. M., Danielski, G. & Orten, J. M. (1961). *Biochem. J.*, **81**, 494.
83. Darcy, D. (1964). *Brit. J. exp. Path.*, **45**, 281; also unpublished experiments.
84. Davydova, S. Ya. & Drozdova, G. A. (1962). *Voprosy Meditsinskoi Khimii*, **8**, 463.
85. De Lamirande, G. (1964). *Cancer Res.*, **24**, 742.
86. Di Mayorca, G. A., Rosenkranz, H. S., Polli, E., Korngold, G. C. & Bendich, A. (1960). *J. natl. Cancer Inst.*, **24**, 1309.
87. Driessens, J., Dupont, A. & Demaille, A. (1963). *Compt. rend. Soc. Biol.*, **157**, 123.
88. Dyer, H. M., Gullino, P. M. & Morris, H. P. (1964). *Cancer Res.*, **24**, 97.
89. Easty, G. C. (1964). *Brit. J. Cancer*, **18**, 368-77.
90. Emmelot, P., Bos, C. J. & Vaz Dias, H. (1964). *Nature, Lond.*, **203**, 77.
91. Farber, E., Shull, K. H., Villa-Trevino, S., Lombardi, B. & Thomas, M. (1964). *Nature, Lond.*, **203**, 34.
92. Feigelson, P., Ultmann, J. E., Harris, S. & Dashman, T. (1959). *Cancer Res.*, **19**, 1230.
93. Furlong, N. B. & Thomann, A. J. (1964). *Proc. Soc. exp. Biol. Med., N.Y.*, **115**, 541.
94. Gellhorn, A., Wagner, M., Rechler, M., Koren, Z. & Benjamin, W. (1964). *Cancer Res.*, **24**, 400 (cf. 480).
95. Gel'shtein, V. I. (1963). *Voprosy Onkologii*, **9**, 61. Translation (1964) in *Fed. Proc.*, **23**, T358.
96. Ghiotto, G., Perona, G., DeDendre, G. & Cortesi, S. (1963). *Brit. J. Haematol.*, **9**, 345.
97. Golder, R. H., Martin-Guzman, G., Jones, J., Goldstein, N. O., Rotenberg, S. & Rutman, R. J. (1964). *Cancer Res.*, **24**, 964.
97a. Goldman, R. D., Kaplan, N. O. & Hall, T. C. (1964). *Cancer Res.*, **24**, 389.
98. Gordon, A. H. (1964). *Biochem. J.*, **90**, 18P.
99. Geren, H. N. & Ghose, T. (1964). *Nature, Lond.*, **201**, 308.
100. Green, H. N. & Savigear, M. (1951). *Brit. med. J.*, **i**, 498.
101. Greenberg, D. M., Blumenthal, G. & Ramadan, M.-E. A. (1964). *Cancer Res.*, **24**, 957.

102. Gustafsson, R. G. & Afzelius, B. A. (1963). *J. natl. Cancer Inst.*, **30**, 1045.
103. Harbers, E. & Nujard, H. (1964). *Abstracts of Communications, 6th Internat. Congr. Biochem.*, p. 58.
104. Harrap, K. R. & Speed, D. E. M. (1964). *Brit. J., Cancer*, **18**, 809-17.
105. Hartman, G. C. & Reid, E. (1964). *Biochem. J.*, **92**, 28P.
105a. Hartman, K-U. & Heidelberger, C. (1961) *J. biol. Chem.*, **236**, 3006.
106. Hawtrey, A. O. & Nourse, L. D. (1964). *Biochm. biophys. Acta*, **80**, 530.
107. Hoagland, M., Scornik, O. A. & Pfefferkorn, L. C. (1964). *Proc. natl. Acad. Sci., Wash.*, **51**, 1185.
108. Hoffman, J., Klein, A., Miheyev, T. & Post, J. (1961). *Arch. Path.*, **71**, 202.
109. Hou, C. T. & Rees, K. R. (1961). *Brit. J. Cancer*, **15**, 624.
110. Hurlbert, R. B. & Kammen, H. O. (1960). *J. biol. Chem.*, **235**, 443.
111. Irving, C. C. & Williard, R. F. (1964). *Cancer Res.*, **24**, 77.
112. Kahler, H. & Moore, B. (1962). *J. natl. Cancer Inst.*, **28**, 561.
113. Kalant, H., Mons, W. & Guttmann, M. (1964). *Canad. J. Physiol. Pharmacol.*, **42**, 25.
114. Kalant, H., Murray, R. K. & Mons, W. (1964). *Cancer Res.*, **24**, 570.
115. Kameswaran, L. & West, G. B. (1961). *J. Pharm. Lond.*, **13**, 191.
116. Kidson, C. & Kirby, K. S. (1964). *Cancer Res.*, **24**, 1604-09.
117. Kielley, R. K. (1963). *Cancer Res.*, **23**, 801.
118. Kizer, D. E., Lovig, C. A., Howell, B. A. & Cox, B. (1964). *Cancer Res.*, **24**, 1050.
119. Kotnis, L. B., Narurkar, M. V. & Sahasrabudhe, M. D. (1962). *Brit. J. Cancer*, **16**, 550.
120. Lafontaine, J. G. & Allard, C. (1964). *J. Cell. Biol.*, **22**, 143.
121. Lampkin-Hibbard, J. M., Mukherjee, K. L. & Heidelberger, C. (1963). *Cancer Res.*, **23**, 468.
122. Larsson, A. (1963). *J. biol. Chem.*, **238**, 3414.
123. Ledoux, L., Brändli, S. & de Paepe, J. C. (1958). *Nature, Lond.*, **181**, 913.
124. LePage, G. A., Junga, I. G. & Bowman, B. (1964). *Cancer Res.*, **24**, 835.
125. Li, S.-O., Chao, T.-C., Chang, H. Y. & Yu, S.-Y. (1963). Cited (1963) in *Chem. Abs.*, **59**, 13203.
126. Loeb, L. A. & Gelboin, H. V. (1963). *Nature, Lond.*, **199**, 809.
127. Luganova, I. S. & Seits, I. F. (1962). *Voprosy Meditsinskoi Khimii*, **8**, 354. Translation (1963) in *Fed. Proc.*, **22**, T1058.
128. McKinney, G. R. & Rundles, R. W. (1956). *Cancer Res.*, **16**, 67.
129. McLean, P., Reid, E. & Gurney, M. W. (1964). *Biochem. J.*, **91**, 464.
130. MacLeod, R. M., King, C. E. & Hollander, V. B. (1963). *Cancer Res.*, **23**, 1045.
131. Magee, P. N. & Lee, K. Y. (1964). *Biochem. J.*, **91**, 35.
132. Maisin, J. H. F. (1964). *Nature, Lond.*, **202**, 202.
133. Maley, F. & Maley, G. F. (1961). *Cancer Res.*, **21**, 1421.
134. Mandel, P., Borkowska, I., Wintzerith, M. & Mandel, L. (1964). *Abstracts, Fed. Europ. Biochem. Socs. Mtg.*, p. 38.

135. MARCHESI, S. L. & SARTORELLI, A. C. (1963). *Cancer Res.*, **23,** 1769.
136. MAVER, M. E. & GRECO, A. E. (1962). *J. natl. Cancer Inst.*, **28,** 1095.
137. MISRA, D. K., HUMPHREYS, S. R., FRIEDKIN, M., GOLDEN, A. & CRAWFORD, E. J. (1961). *Nature, Lond.*, **189,** 39.
138. MIURA, Y. & MORIYAMA, A. (1961). *J. Biochem. Tokyo.*, **50,** 355 (see also p. 362).
139. MOORE, B. W. & ANGELETTI, P. U. (1961). *Ann. N.Y. Acad. Sci.*, **94,** 659.
140. MORRIS, A. L., SCOTT, D. B. M. & REISKIN, A. B. (1961). *Cancer Res.*, **21,** 1352.
141. MOTOC, F. & CONSTANTINESCU, S. (1962). *Acad. Rep. Populare Romine, Studii Cercetari Biochim.*, **5,** 91. Cited (1962) in *Chem. Abs.*, **57,** 3917.
142. MURAMATSU, M. (1961). *Gann,* **52,** 135.
143. NAGASAWA, H. T. & OSTERAAS, A. J. (1964). *Biochem. Pharmacol.*, **13,** 713.
144. NATORI, Y. & TARVER, H. (1964). *Abstracts, 6th Internat. Congr. Biochem.*, 77.
145. NEBERT, D. W. & MASON, H. S. (1964). *Biochim. biophys. Acta,* **86,** 415.
146. NEISH, W. J. P. & RYLETT, A. (1963). *Biochem. Pharmacol.*, **12,** 893.
147. NIGAM, V. N., MACDONALD, H. L. & CANTERO, A. (1962). *Cancer Res.*, **22,** 131.
148. NIKOLOV, T. K. & KHADZHIOLOV, A. A. (1961). *Biokhimia,* **26,** 523; Translation in *Biochemistry,* U.S.S.R., **26,** 464.
149. NUNNARI, A., CALAFATO, M., BELFIORE, F. & ROMANO, F. (1963). *Boll. Soc. ital. Biol. sper.*, **39,** 772. Cited (1963) in *Chem. Abs.*, **59,** 10598.
150. O'NEAL, M. A. & GRIFFIN, A. C. (1963). *Cancer Res.*, **23,** 628.
151. PATERSON, A. R. P. & HORI, A. (1963). *Canad. J. Biochem. Physiol.*, **41,** 1339.
152. PERAINO, C. & PITOT, H. C. (1962). *Biochem. biophys. Acta,* **62,** 585.
153. PEREVOSTCHIKOVA, K. A., GOLUBOVICH, L. M. & KAVERINA, A. F. (1962). *Voprosy Meditsinskoi Khimii,* **8,** 532. Translation (1963) in *Fed. Proc.*, **22,** T1049.
154. POLLI, E. E. & SHOOTER, K. V. (1958). *Biochem. J.*, **69,** 398.
155. POTTER, V. R., PITOT, H. C., ONO, T. & MORRIS, H. P. (1960). *Cancer Res.*, **20,** 1255.
156. PRADHAN, S. N., WEST, W. L., BAIRD, C. M. & STEWARD, J. D. (1961). *Cancer Res.*, **21,** 984.
157. RABBI, A., CALDARERA, C. M. & BARBIROLI, B. (1962). *Boll. Soc. ital. Biol. sper.*, **38,** 1909. Cited (1964) in *Chem. Abs.*, **60,** 4591.
158. RECHCIGL, M. & SIDRANSKY, H. (1962). *J. natl. Cancer Inst.*, **28,** 1411.
159. REDDY, D. V. N., BREIGER, H. & ORCHEN, M. (1957). *Cancer Res.*, **17,** 677.
160. REES, K. R., ROWLAND, G. F. & ROSS, H. F. (1962). *Biochem. J.*, **82,** 347.
161. REGE, D. V. & SREENIVASAN, A. (1962). *Ind. J. med. Res.*, **50,** 502.

162. Reichard, P., Skold, O., Klein, G. Révész, L. & Magnusson, P.-H. (1962). *Cancer Res.*, **22,** 235.
163. Reid, E. (1964). *Brit. J. Cancer*, **18,** 179 (see also p. 172).
164. Reid, J. D., Riley, J. F. & Shepherd, D. M. (1963). *Biochem. Pharmacol.*, **12,** 1151.
165. Roberts, J. J. & Warwick, G. P. (1964). *Biochem. J.*, **93,** 18P.
166. Roberts, S. & White, A. (1953). *Endocrinology*, **52,** 372.
167. Robinson, E. A., Kalckar, H. M. & Troedsson, H. (1963). *Biochem. biophys. res. Commun.*, **13,** 313.
168. Roth, J. S. (1963). *J. theoret. Biol.*, **4,** 113.
169. Roth, J. S., Hilton, S. & Morris, H. P. (1964). *Cancer Res.*, **24,** 294.
170. Rothberg, S. & Van Scott, E. J. (1964). *J. invest. Dermatol.*, **42,** 141.
171. Rubenchik, B. L. (1963). *Dopovidi Akad. Nauk. ukr. RSR*, 241; Ukr. *Biokhim. Zh.*, **35,** 352. Cited (1963) in *Chem. Abs.*, **59,** 10589 and 14408.
172. Rubin, E., Masuko, K., Goldfarb, S. & Zak, F. G. (1964). *Proc. Soc. exp. Biol. Med., N.Y.*, **115,** 381.
173. Sahasrabudhe, M. B., Apte, B. K., Aboobaker, V. S. & Jagaraman, R. (1962). *Biochem. biophys. res. Commun.*, **7,** 173.
174. Saidov, S. M. (1958). *Byull ekosptl. Biol. i Med.*, **45,** 45. Translation in *Bull. exp. Biol. Med.* (Consultants Bureau Inc.), same pagination; cited (1959) in *Chem. Abs.*, **53,** 9440.
175. Sangster, C. L., Schochet, S. S. & Farber, E. (1963). *Cancer Res.*, **23,** 1069.
176. Sartorelli, A. C. (1964). *Nature, Lond.*, **203,** 877.
177. Saukkonen, J. J. (1956). *Ann. Med. exp. Biol. Fenn*, **45,** Suppl. **3,** 1.
178. Schapira, F., Dreyfus, J.-C. & Schapira, G. (1963). *Nature, Lond.*, **200,** 995.
179. Schneider, W. C. & Behki, R. M. (1963). *J. biol. Chem.*, **238,** 3565.
180. Seed, J. (1963). *Nature, Lond.*, **198,** 147.
181. Shapira, J., Bornstein, I., Wells, W. & Winzler, R. J. (1961). *Cancer Res.*, **21,** 265.
182. Shull, K. H., Villa-Trevino, S. & Oler, A. (1964). *Abstracts, 6th Internat. Congr. Biochem.*, 86.
183. Silber, R., Huennekens, F. M. & Gabrio, B. W. (1963). *J. clin. Invest.*, **42,** 1908.
184. Sköld, O. (1963). *Biochim. biophys Acta*, **76,** 160.
185. Smith, K. C. & Kaplan, H. S. (1961). *Cancer Res.*, **21,** 1148.
186. Sorof, S., Young, E. M., McBridge, R. A. & Binder, C. L. (1964). *Abstracts, 6th Internat. Congr. Biochem.*, 405.
187. Stekol, J. A., Bedrak, E., Mody, U., Burnette, N. & Somerville, C. (1963). *J. biol. Chem.*, **238,** 469.
188. Stirpe, F. & Aldridge, W. N. (1961). *Biochem. J.*, **80,** 481.
189. Sunderman, F. W. (1963). *Amer. J. clin. Path.*, **39,** 549.
190. Suzuki, I. (1962). *Sapporo Igaku Zasshi*, **21,** 327 & 352. Cited (1964) in *Chem. Abs.*, **51,** 2286.
191. Sydow, G. (1963). *Acta biol. med. germ.*, **10,** 590.

192. Szent-Györgyi, A., Hegyeli, A. & McLaughlin, J. A. (1963). *Proc. natl. Acad. Sci., Wash.*, **49**, 878.
193. Thierig, M. & Willinghagen, R. G. J. (1963). *Nature, Lond.*, **197**, 1312.
194. Trams, E. G., Nadkarni, M. V. & Smith, P. K. (1961). *Cancer Res.*, **21**, 560 & 567.
195. Traub, A., Kaufmann, E. & Ginzburg-Tietz, Y. (1964). *Exptl. Cell. Res.*, **34**, 371.
196. Turner, M. K. & Reid, E. (1964). *Nature, Lond.*, **203**, 1174.
197. Vorbrodt, A. (1960). *Bull. Acad. polon. Sci. Ser. sci. biol.*, **8**, 489. Cited (1961) in *Chem. Abs.*, **55**, 9599.
198. Vorbrodt, A. (1961). *J. Histochem. Cytochem.*, **9**, 647.
199. Wagle, S. R., Morris, H. P. & Weber, G. (1963). *Biochim. biophys. Acta*, **78**, 783.
200. Webb, T. E., Blobel, G. & Potter, V. R. (1964). *Proc. Amer. Assocn. Cancer Res.*, **24**, 1229.
201. Weber, G. & Morris, H. P. (1963). *Cancer Res.*, **23**, 987 & 995.
202. Weber, M. (1960). *Acta med. polon.*, **1**, 27. Cited (1961) in *Chem. Abs.*, **55**, 3781.
203. Wheeler, G. P., Alexander, J. A., Dodson, A. S., Briggs, S. D. & Morris, H. P. (1962). *Cancer Res.*, **22**, 769.
204. Whitcutt, J. M. & Roth, J. S. (1964). *Biochim. biophys. Acta*, **87**, 380.
205. Wilczok, T. (1961). *Neoplasma*, **8**, 345.
206. Werkheiser, W. V. & Visser, D. W. (1955). *Cancer Res.*, **15**, 644.
207. Wu, C. & Bauer, J. M. (1962). *Cancer Res.*, **22**, 1239.
208. Wulff, V. J., Quastler, H. & Sherman, F. G. (1962). *Proc. natl. Acad. Sci., Wash.*, **48**, 1373.
209. Yasuda, S. (1963). *Osaka Daigaku Igaku Zasshi*, **15**, 193. Cited (1964) in *Chem. Abs.*, **60**, 3343.
210. Yunis, A. & Arimura, G. K. (1964). *Cancer Res.*, **24**, 489.
211. Zamecnik, P. C. & Stephenson, M. L. (1947). *Cancer Res.*, **7**, 326.
212. Zbarskii, I. B. & Georgiev, G. P. (1963). *Vopr. Onkol.*, **9**, 16. Cited in *Chem. Abs.*, **59**, 14405; see also (1956) *Chem. Abs.*, **50**, 10899.
213. Zbarskii, I. B. & Karuzina, N. P. (1959). *Byull. Ekxptl. Biol. i. Med.*, **48**, 65. Cited (1961) in *Chem. Abs.*, **55**, 1881.
214. Zbarsky, S. H., Hori, A. & Findlay, B. S. (1958). *Canad. J. Biochem. Physiol.*, **36**, 1185.
215. Zimmerman, M. & Celozzi, E. (1961). *Nature, Lond.*, **191**, 1014.
216. Zimmerman, M. & Seidenberg, J. (1964). *J. biol. Chem.*, **239**, 2618.

Index

The emphasis in the Index is on biochemical phenomena; thus, azo dyes are not listed with respect to their carcinogenicity (see Contents list) or to their metabolic effects. Definitions as given early in Chapter 1 are not indexed. For enzymes, Code Numbers are given parenthetically, except where a number cannot be allotted with reasonable certainty.